FROM
WHITE KNUCKLES
TO
COCKPIT COOL

by Ava and David
Carmichael
ILLUSTRATED
by
Lupe Blea

AERO PUBLISHERS, INC.
329 West Aviation Road, Fallbrook, CA 92028

David
Carmichael

Acknowledgements

Jeppesen Sanderson, for use of the Jeppesen PJ-1 Plotter and the Long Beach Approach Plate, Copyright 1976 Jeppesen Sanderson, Inc.

Piper Aircraft Corporation.

U.S. Department of Commerce, National Oceanic and Atmospheric Administration, National Ocean Survey.

Southwest Air Rangers, El Paso, Texas.

Gibbs Flying Service, Inc.

PDQ Computer Co.

Cessna Aircraft Co.

Beech Aircraft Corporation.

Ninety-Nines, Inc.

Library of Congress Cataloging in Publication Data
Carmichael, Ava.

    From white knuckles to cockpit cool.

    1. Private flying.   I. Carmichael, David,
joint author. II. Title.
TL721.4.C36   1977   629.132'5217   77-83055
ISBN 0-8168-5850-0

Table of Contents

A. Glossary of Terms, Contractions and Acronyms
B. Line Boy Checklist
C. Remain Overnight (RON) Checklist
D. Survival Kit
E. Airplane "First Aid" Kit
F. Density Altitude Table
G. International Morse Code and Phonetic Alphabet
H. Bahamian Nav-Com Frequencies
I. VORs in Mexico
J. Mexico Checklist
K. Emergency Equipment for Flight Over a "Sparsely Settled Area" in Canada
L. Loading Checklist
M. Tools the Pilot Uses

WARNING: *Charts reproduced are not to scale, and are not to be used for navigation.*

Preface

Helping with a successful airplane flight is much like whipping up a gourmet dinner, except that when you have finished you are likely to have arrived at some new and exciting place where someone else has done the cooking!

No matter how liberated the woman, analogies that relate to the home are probably understandable and have been used periodically in this volume. Cooking and flying involve weights, temperature, timing, planning and patience. Consider apologies already made if portions of the book seem elementary. During a trip through ground school, the principal author would have been delighted if someone had insulted her intelligence enough to tell her "what the heck was going on" when terms like VFR, ADF, and VOR were being tossed about with great facility by the Airline Transport Rated instructor.

A major purpose of this book is to take the traditional passenger's right seat and make it less of a "hot seat;" to make the flying companion a helpful observer; to provide a second pair of eyes and hands (although success in this endeavor will result in the pilot expecting the aid of six eyes, four hands, and the brain of a computer); as well as to create a knowledgeable admirer when the pilot masterfully conquers time and space.

This "Simplified Cordon Bleu Cookbook" for the white knuckles set did not spring full grown from ashes like Phoenix, but combines the cooperation and help of a large number of pilots and their companions. It is an outgrowth of a series of seminars for flying companions given in San Diego with the assistance of dozens of friends. Particular mention should be directed to the Ninety-Nines, an incorporated organization of women pilots with an active group of chapters in southern California. The personnel of the General Aviation District Office of the Federal Aviation Administration in San Diego also merit praise. Bill Glenn, Bob Griscom, and Don Best were ever helpful. So many aided that it is hard to single out certain women pilots of the Ninety-Nines of the San Diego area, but Betty Wharton, Marilyn Eimers, Linda Dutcher, Shirley Wolf, Diane Stocklin, Beatrice Wheeler, Penny Lowe, Camilla Hutson, Margaret Parsons, Ruth Ebey, Joanruth Baumann, Mary Eggar, Lynn Briggs, Dottie Helm, Carol Shigley, and Pat Osmon all did yeoman service in presenting the seminars. Credit should also be given to the ever-patient J.B. Melton and to the memory of Chuck Stuart who shepherded me through flight instruction once my appetite had been whetted by being a flying companion. Our daughters, Heather and Linda, spent hours working with my faltering grammar, and the entire family showed great indulgence. Finally, my thanks for over two thousand safe and enjoyable hours of flying with my Powder Puff Derby partner, Wanda Cummings, and my pilot-husband, David.

Ava Carmichael
La Jolla, California

UNDERSTANDING YOUR PEGASUS

A girl can't be too careful these days! After accepting an invitation to "Go get on your flying togs" she may find herself in a bewildering situation when a group of friends start throwing around terms like "slip indicator," "holding pattern," "unusual attitude," "preparing for the approach," "Love Field," "stacked," "magnetic attraction," "warming trend," as well as other unexpected and seemingly Bacchanalian terms. If, driven by insecurity after hearing such phrases, she happens to pick up Erica Jong's **Fear of Flying,** further shocks await our less than willing passenger.

Facetiousness aside, flying can be fun and this little volume is meant to stimulate confidence by familiarity with the terms, techniques, rationale, and joys of being a passenger and a participant in flight in light aircraft. No attempt is made to teach piloting skills. If there is an area of emphasis, it relates to safety. It is the firm contention of the authors that flight in well-maintained general aviation aircraft by thoroughly trained pilots is safe; but that the level of safety can be increased by assistance and support offered by a knowledgeable flying companion. In nearly 2000 hours of private flying in a number of aircraft this hypothesis has been tested on several occasions. As assurance builds, so will appreciation of the advantages "taking to the air" allows. It is a compliment to the pilot to be interested in the skills he has acquired. It is also reassuring to find that you are able not only to understand but also to significantly contribute to the pleasure of flight. Who knows? Like the authors, you may find this attitude the first step in a move from the right seat to the traditional pilot's left seat and the exciting title of "pilot-in-command"!

When your pilot marshals arguments to justify the expense of further honing his skills you may feel like humming a few bars of "It seems to me I've heard that song before . . .," but before you turn a deaf ear to the music, read on a bit.

From White Knuckles to Cockpit Cool

The modern general aviation aircraft is not only fast, comfortable, relatively economical in seat miles per gallon of fuel; but also beautiful in flight. This is a modern Piper Aztec F.

The idea that "God would have given us wings if He had wanted us to fly" is still quite prevalent, particularly at the time of one's first flight in a light aircraft. It is still common to hear someone boast that "nobody is going to get me off of the ground and into one of those things," particularly if there has been a lurid newspaper account of some accident involving an aircraft.

There still is an element of mysticism about powered flight and little recognition by the general public that "those things" have come a long way since the "wonderful men in their flying machines." The militant non-flyer continues to view powered flight in terms of the Wright Brothers, John J. Montgomery, Louis Bleriot and others who paved the way to the safe and efficient aircraft of today. General aviation aircraft come under even more cynical scrutiny by these non-flying "authorities" who still equate modern business and pleasure airplanes with Snoopy's Sopwith Camel of World War I vintage. Such comparisons have about the same legitimacy as relating the scrub-board of our grandmother with the totally automatic home laundry of the modern era. Thanks to reliable companies who manufacture airplanes, a large segment of the American public who recognize their efficiency, and tight state and Federal regulations, we now have the staggering total of 750,000 active pilots; nearly 175,000 aircraft; nearly 1000 air traffic control towers and Flight Service Stations; and a record of approximately 5,000,000 people carried by air annually in the United States alone. In the general aviation sector in the last year for which figures were available there were only 2.09 fatalities per 100,000 aircraft hours. It is inescapable! Planes do fly safely and, like inside plumbing, they are here to stay.

As a pleasure vehicle, the modern airplane has much to offer. A long weekend for San Diegans can mean such things as Las Vegas with exciting "Big Name" entertainment, Mammoth for skiing or summer hiking, San Francisco for

gourmet dining. Another possibility is a "round the world weekend tour" to London Bridge at Lake Havasu, the Danish village of Solvang, the Mexican handicraft and excellent Mexican and Chinese food of Mexicali. It is even unnecessary to take the airplane into Mexico for this trip as you land at Calexico, California, and simply walk a few yards across the border into Mexicali.

Look at the charts of your area and, with a little courage on your part, those "eight hours by car" places you have always wanted to visit are "just down the road a bit." You will also notice in your pilot a peculiar kind of release of tension and anxiety that occurs as he lifts off of the runway for even a short flight devoted to air-sightseeing. There is for him a unique sense of satisfaction in fully mastering the complexities of the modern airplane and its diverse instruments. If your family likes to hunt or fish, new vistas are opened. Distant sporting events are within easy reach. Vacations are lengthened. We had a terrific extra four

days added to a Klamath Falls, Oregon, camping trip by flying to the site with all camping equipment stowed in the plane, renting a car and taking off for a blackberry picking good time. Our "mini-vacations" to Borrego Springs are much longer and more fun when it is 30 minutes portal-to-portal instead of a two hour drive over twisting roads rising from sea level to 5,000 feet and descending again to the desert floor. When our daughter was at the University of Redlands she was 40 minutes by air, or three hours by car on a freeway fraught with a history of fatal accidents.

Still shaking your head no??? Let me relate a few more experiences. We have made multiple trips to take unused medicines to the Direct Relief Foundation in Santa Barbara for distribution to underprivileged countries. It is a flight of slightly over two hours round-trip by air, and ten hours at times of low traffic density through Los Angeles if accomplished by car. An emergency trip to Lubbock, Texas, began at the notification of the

From White Knuckles to Cockpit Cool

emergency and was completed in less than six hours. This may seem like a long time, but anyone checking airline schedules between San Diego and Lubbock, and coupling this with the inevitable waits in crowded airports and for baggage handling, would get this into proper perspective. We made a necessary business trip to the East and had delightful stops to visit family in Texas, Kansas City, and an old University roommate in Madisonville, Kentucky. Entertaining a "visiting fireman" from the midwest by a quick luncheon flight to the excellent restaurant at the airport on Catalina Island made his trip memorable and our day pleasant. Suffice it to say, the extra legs the aircraft gives can be translated into a fuller life.

At least a verse or two of the following "hard sell" you are sure to have heard. As a business device hundreds of companies as well as individual businessmen have recognized the versatility of a personal airplane in accomplishing commercial and professional tasks. With the recent constriction in routes by the commercial airlines as well as fewer flights, this has become even more important. Think of the salesman servicing rural areas. Look at airline schedules for small cities in middle America and ponder the long waits, cars rented, hard drives, and overnight stops necessitated in reaching the rural towns where his orders may originate and his products are primarily marketed. Then pick up a Kansas City or Memphis Sectional Chart and view the host of airports scattered all over the map. A quick flight; a call to Unicom to contact his prospect will result in no lost time, and the customer is complimented by a face-to-face discussion. In a day many such stops can be made, and a quick flight home at the conclusion of a productive trip may result in more time for family interests. Our plane has been used many times to extend medical ser-

vice. One more dramatic example was a flight with a surgical associate to put in an emergency electronic heart pacemaker. The service was not available in the small city where the patient was hospitalized and he was far too sick to be transferred to San Diego.

I feel sure that we have repeated most of his old arguments, but stay with us a little longer for our avowed effort of familiarization.

How does the airplane fly? Just as the old scrub-board and the modern washing machine both use the technique of agitation of water and the use of a cleansing agent, the principles of flight in the time of Bleriot and today remain the same. They have, however, undergone the equivalent level of refinement that has the modern kitchen. In short, the wings provide lift; the engines deliver thrust;

and these are packaged in such a way that the opposing forces of gravity and drag are completely overcome. The air frame is "streamlined" to reduce drag. The engines are powerful and efficient; built to tolerances never imagined in the commercial automobile. The instruments are reliable and "back-up" devices are present for almost any function should a mechanical or electronic failure occur. Not only have safety factors dominated the attention of aircraft engineers; they have been of prime importance to governmental regulatory bodies. As described elsewhere in this volume, a whole network of emergency techniques has been developed and perfected. Performed by competent pilots, and particularly when assisted by an informed flying companion, modern flight in general aviation aircraft is safe and fun.

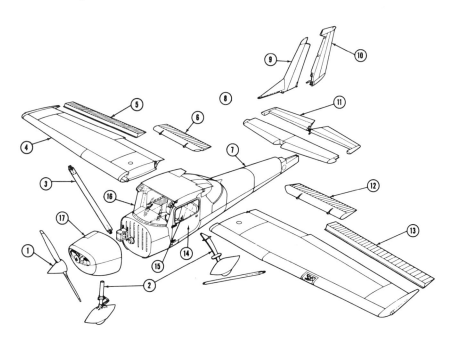

The Main Parts of an Airplane

1. Propeller	10. Rudder
2. Landing Gear	11. Elevator
3. Wing Strut	12. Left Wing Flap
4. Wing	13. Left Wing Aileron
5. Right Wing Aileron	14. Door
6. Right Wing Flap	15. Seat
7. Fuselage	16. Windshield
8. Horizontal Stabilizer	17. Engine Cowl
9. Fin and Dorsal	

From White Knuckles to Cockpit Cool

Terms you will hear as you learn more about aviation are listed in the appendix, but in considering principles of flight some will be introduced now. The wing has "lift" and this is generated by the intense stream of air flowing over the top of the wing rather than the air pushing the wing up from below. In addition, lift is derived from the "prop blast" generated by the whirling propellers pulling the aircraft through the sky. This is the principal reason for a propeller-driven craft being more quickly responsive to full throttle than a jet. With the jet, there is no prop blast to quickly increase lift.

A portion of the back or "trailing edge" of the wing can be seen to move when the yoke (wheel) is moved to the right or left. This is the aileron and changes the direction of the air flowing over the wing, resulting in a turn. Another portion of the trailing edge of the wing is given over to the "flaps" which are really a form of air brake with a dual purpose. Flaps both slow speed and increase lift. Dependent upon the degree of flap extension, the "lift" portion can be accentuated when needed for takeoff from a short field, or

the "air brake" function can be used when landing in a limited area. The vertical portion of the tail also has a segment that moves. This is the rudder and is actuated by pedals on the floor of the cabin. The rudder is used to keep the plane in "trim"; that is, flying in a balanced position in relation to gravity and the drift of the wind. Turns with the ailerons are coordinated by gentle rudder movement to make a smooth, efficient change in direction. The horizontal portion of the tail is known as the stabilizer and either a part or all may be made to move by retracting or pushing forward on the yoke. The moving part is known as the elevator. This changes the attitude of the aircraft, causing a gentle dive with forward movement of the yoke, or a climb by pulling back.

The flying companion should have the pilot give her the "feel" of flight during straight and level operation allowing her to change the position of the ailerons in a turn; feel the effect of gentle rudder actuation; and both climb and dive by movement of the yoke. It will seem remarkably easy and in a properly trimmed airplane it should be.

TOOLS THE PILOT USES

A number of indispensable materials are necessary to properly plan a flight. These are summarized here and more completely explained in subsequent chapters.

CHARTS

1. **Sectional Charts:** There are 37 such charts designed for visual navigation (VFR) of slow or medium speed aircraft. A new chart is issued for each section about every six months; however, the dates of issue are staggered so that you need not replace all at one time. These are the most detailed charts available. They contain all data necessary to plan a safe flight except NOTAMS. These are the charts that you as a flying companion will be using. A complete discussion of their proper application will be found in the chapter devoted to "Planning the Flight."

The face of the Sectional Chart, with its label signifying a major city contains a wealth of information allowing the novice to learn to "read" the chart. Use the Sectional Scale when measuring this chart.

The WAC (World Aeronautical Chart) uses the same symbols as the Sectional Chart. Since this chart covers a much greater area you must use the WAC Scale on the plotter to make your measurements.

2. **World Aeronautical Charts (WAC):** These provide a standard series of charts covering landing areas of the world at a size and scale convenient for navigation by aircraft of moderate speed. There are only 11 of these to chart the same area covered in 37 Sectional Charts. Parts of Mexico and Canada are also included. It is therefore obvious that they could not contain the detail covered by the Sectional Charts. Except in a flight planned for the involved parts of Mexico where Sectional Charts are not available, the flying companion will prefer Sectionals.

3. **Local Charts:** Many Sectional Charts include an inset of heavily congested areas. They are helpful when crossing or landing in one of these areas. It is, however, necessary to reorient your thinking to the different scale used on these charts as you will seem to move very rapidly across them. **VFR TERMINAL AREA CHARTS** are available for the airports which have a Terminal Control Area.

4. **En Route Low Altitude Charts:** These offer aeronautical information for en route navigation under instrument flight rules (IFR) in the airspace below 18,000 feet where most general aviation aircraft operate. They are helpful in flight planning for VFR flight as they offer much condensed information. These charts contain principal radio data, and are a quick reference for OMNI frequencies, magnetic headings, and distances between navigational aids. No detailed terrain information is included; however, minimum en route altitudes (MEA) are listed and ensure adequate terrain clearance on airways.

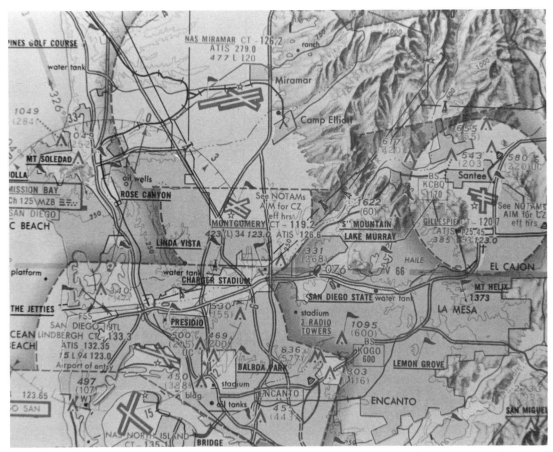

The Local Chart shows landmarks in much greater detail. This Chart of the San Diego area shows the location of the two military airports (Miramar and North Island); the commercial airfield (Lindbergh Field); and the two major city General Aviation airports (Montgomery and Gillespie).

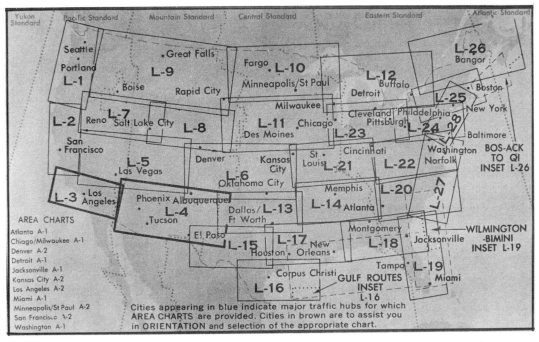

Bold-faced heavy lines indicate the area covered by the specific En Route Low Altitude Chart.

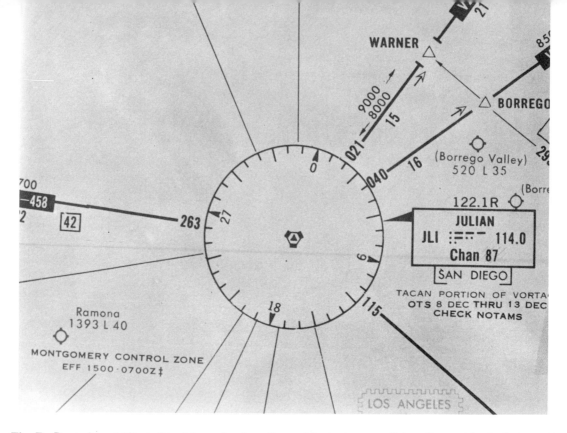

The En Route Low Altitude Chart is predominantly used for instrument flying. For rapid calculations of headings, distances, safe altitudes, and OMNI frequencies it is a marvel of efficiency. Airports are designated but no terrain information is given, and these charts are of no other practical use in pilotage.

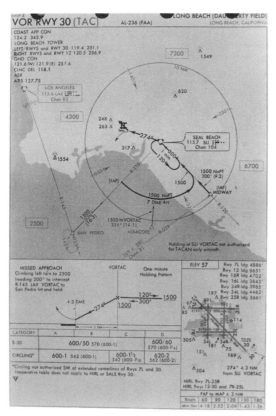

An Approach Plate is a mine of information describing all of the data necessary to prepare for landing.

5. **Approach Plates:** While not in the strictest sense a chart, these are extremely helpful in landing. All information for landing at airports with any instrument capability is included. By virtue of their importance, a detailed chapter on the use of approach plates is found in subsequent pages of this book.

AIRPORT GUIDES

One of the best guides is published by the Aircraft Owners and Pilots Association (AOPA) entitled *AOPA'S AIRPORTS U.S.A.* A new edition is published annually and included are data on nearly 13,000 landing sites. The book is a gem and in it may be found: weather and flight information telephone numbers, a geographical designator map with common terms used in aviation weather forecasts, time zones, great circle distances between major U.S. cities, U.S. international airports and landing rights airports, a discussion of mountain flying, aeronautical charts, terminal control area graphics, airport diagrams, state-by-state listing of airports, seaplane bases and heliports with data as to geography and facilities, a landing fee key, and an alphabetical cross reference index of airports. Of particular interest to the flying companion are the types of transportation available from the airport to the community; availability of food service at the airport or its environs; overnight lodging available; and nearby recreational areas. This book is highly recommended!!!

PLOTTER

These instruments are like toothbrushes and every pilot or navigator has his favorite. All are similar, but each has the same basic information presented in a slightly different manner. You must become very familiar with this tool as it will be used during the planning of the flight as well as en route.

One feature plotters all seem to have in common is the plastic material used for their construction. They melt, bend, and become unusable when allowed to remain in a hot plane. When you "tie down" for the night, take your plotter to the motel. In fact, it is wise to carry the whole flight bag. That "perfect flight" you planned at home may now be shrouded in clouds,

obscured by blowing dust, or at the reverse end of a tunnel of headwinds. It will possibly be necessary to plan another route after discussion with the Guru at the Flight Service Station. Don't ask the pilot if the flight bag is needed. Take it along!

The plotter is used to plot an intended flight course, establish flight plan "check points," accurately measure course lines and directions, plot lines of position, as well as plot true and magnetic North lines.

For the purpose of this book, we are going to leave the esoteric to the pilot and be concerned with the first three capabilities.

The plotter has a "Sectional Chart Scale" and a "WAC Scale." It is important for you to look carefully at the markings to determine which is the "Sectional Scale" since this is the one you will be using in the majority of situations. You must also identify the scales that measure "nautical miles" and "statute miles." In fact, it is important to be familiar with all of the writing on the face of the plotter in order to be fully comfortable with this vital tool. In the chapters devoted to flight planning you will use the plotter as you actually plan a flight.

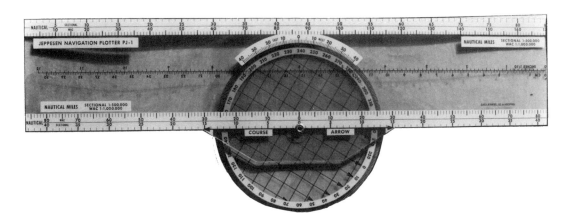

The plotter is used as a straight edge. It also contains a number of different scales for measuring miles and headings.

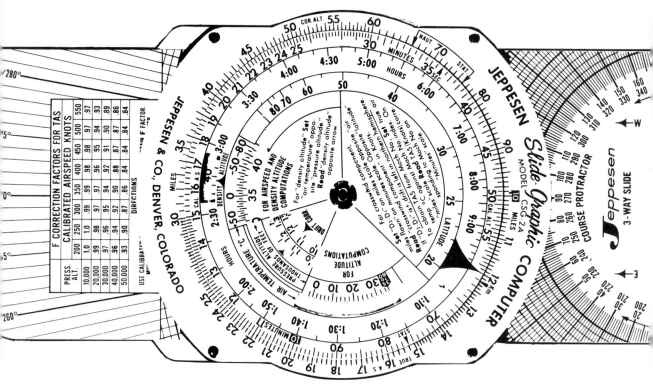

The Aviation Computer presents a frightening appearance to the mathematically uninitiated, but many of its functions are disarmingly simple and quickly learned.

COMPUTER

Computers are similar to plotters in two respects: there seem to be an endless variety, and every pilot has his favorite. They may be made of plastic, metal, or a combination of the two. In characteristic types there is a calculator or arithmetic side and a wind side. Almost all computers offer a book giving detailed explanations of typical problems. Included in this book is a chapter describing common and practical uses of the computer well within the range of any flying companion. Do **not** throw up your hands when you are first confronted with this instrument. "One step at a time" is truly good advice and the aviation computer is no more complex than oven timers and other accoutrements of the modern kitchen.

With these tools available and understood, the apprenticeship ends and you are ready to actually assist in flight planning as well as the flight itself.

THE SECTIONAL CHART

Like a novice cook first reading a gourmet cookbook, your initial attempt to decipher a Sectional Chart may be discouraging. However, if you proceed one step at a time, just as in studying a recipe, you will master this apparent hodgepodge of lines, symbols, colors, and instructions. A Sectional Chart is a map containing detailed airplane navigational data. In flight under Visual Flight Rules this chart is the primary source of navigational information and although the information contained has been the subject of a great deal of study by the pilot, an interested flying companion can be of inestimable help to the pilot if she is able to keep accurate track of the progress of the flight. The Sectional Chart with its radio aids, airport locations, airway routes, surface features of the earth, as well as a host of other information is the "open sesame" to the technique of *pilotage*—navigation by visual reference to terrain and landmarks.

Because of the importance of the Sectional Chart the technique in this chapter will be to ask the reader to obtain a recent Sectional and use it constantly as this chapter is studied. For convenience we have chosen the Los Angeles Sectional Chart and will refer to it, but the important information can be understood with any Sectional at hand.

At this point you will have your first wrestling match with a Sectional Chart. Every pilot and navigator devises his own technique of folding these awkward maps, and to this point no one has a unitarian answer. Various plastic folders are available into which the Sectional can be inserted with the desired part of the chart in view. On short flights these are fine, but on a long cross country it merely introduces another folding monster to contend with in the limited space of an airplane cockpit.

Before allowing the neatly folded map to begin its attempt to fill the room, find

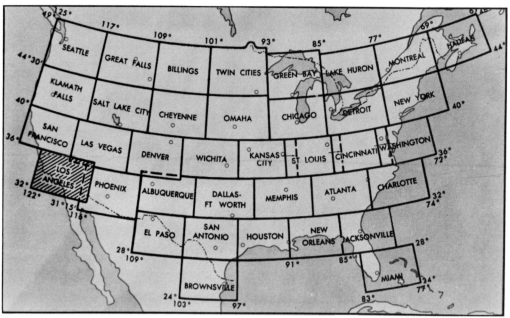

The specific Sectional Chart is shown as a cross-hatched box. Contiguous charts are identified, and this facilitates flight planning.

the face sheet entitled in the instance of the Los Angeles Sectional, "Los Angeles Sectional Aeronautical Chart, Scale 1:500,000." The initial paragraphs are important in that the magenta lines describe the date this chart is obsolete. If your chart is out of date, it is important to bring this to the attention of the pilot. In this day of the "sudden high rise" apartment and of taller and taller TV towers, an aged Sectional Chart is poor economics. Fortunately the charts become obsolete on a staggered schedule so that the blow to the exchequer is not severe. These initial paragraphs also contain the line, "Consult appropriate NOTAMs and Flight Information Publications for supplemental data and current information." This is another important reminder to both the pilot and the navigator that things do change, and there are other sources of ready information.

A line map of the United States appears next. It is divided into thirty-seven parts or sections, thus the name Sectional. By viewing this diagram you become familiar with the names of all Sectionals available for the United States. Observe that one section is shaded. This is the chart you are currently holding, and by correlating this with your planned route of flight other needed charts become obvious.

The color column depicts the key to the altitudes covered on the Sectional. The shades of green, yellow, and orange are subtle, but you will quickly develop a good "eye." The Los Angeles Sectional has eight shades of color, topped by the large number 11502. This number denotes the maximum elevation of any terrain on the chart. At the bottom of the column the number -235 is seen, indicating that the lowest terrain is actually well below sea level. Heights from sea level to 1000 feet are pale green; 1000 to 2000 feet a darker green; 2000 to 3000 feet an ivory shade. Elevations above 3000 feet show a color change at 2000 foot increments, with the higher altitudes showing progressively deeper shades of orange.

At this point you should open your chart to view the shadings of color; the contour lines, and the oblong boxes with ticked lines representing lines of latitude and longitude. In each such box you will note large numbers in the center. This number, i.e. 7°, indicates in charts prepared after July 1977, that the maximum elevation in that area does not exceed 7000 feet. On the face sheet of charts antedating the change from Maximum Terrain Elevation to Maximum Elevation Figures, a legend states ". . . BUT DO NOT INCLUDE ELEVATIONS OF VERTICAL OBSTRUCTIONS." Such old charts must be checked for man-made impediments to safe flight. The new charts obviate this scrutiny. All charts continue to show Critical elevations with a black dot, and approximate elevations have a small "x" preceding the number. The latter are rare in the conterminous United States.

The chart could now be turned so that the page entitled, "Los Angeles Aeronautical Symbols" lies in front of you. Here we find the symbols and abbreviations used on the face of the map. Since the key is a part of each chart, it is not necessary to memorize them all.

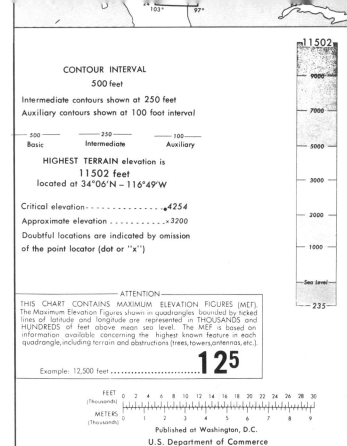

Terrain information is individualized on each Sectional Chart. This Los Angeles Sectional indicates that there is no natural obstacle to navigation at any point on the chart which exceeds 11,502 feet. A metric scale is provided.

The top portion of each Sectional Chart is laden with information describing the multiple forms of airports, as well as aerodrome data.

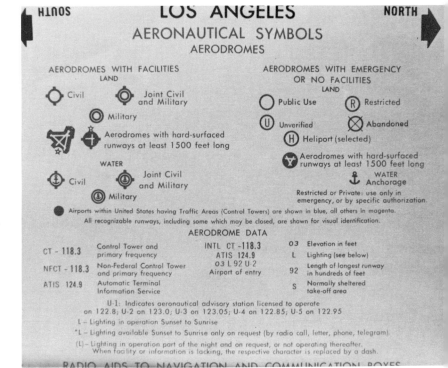

From White Knuckles to Cockpit Cool

Carefully review the material about aerodromes. The double circle denoting a military airport is important in flight planning. Unless there is a serious emergency or there has been prior written permission, a civilian pilot should not use such an airport. An unscheduled landing at a military field is against the law and will require some tall explaining! At night such airports are identified by their rotating beacons which flash in a sequence of two white flashes followed by a green flash. A civilian airport will alternately flash white and green.

A glance at the map will show that aerodrome symbols not only differ in configuration, but also in color. Those marked in blue have a Control Tower, and those in magenta do not. A star at the twelve o'clock position signifies a rotating light. The knobs on the circle denote a civilian airport with sophisticated facilities, and if the circle is solid with runways shown in relief, you can be sure that runways are hard surfaced and at least 1500 feet in length. If the circle is smooth, but is filled in with blue or magenta and shows runways, it too will indicate a hard surfaced runway of 1500 feet or greater.

A flying companion will soon learn that the term "Aerodromes with Emergency or no Facilities" may be misleading. Such an airport would be pictured in magenta on the Sectional. It is true that there may be no radio facilities other than Unicom at these fields, but some of the best restaurants, nicest powder rooms, and most enticing nearby resorts may offset the lack of sophisticated navigation aids. Even some of the airports designated by an open circle indicative of a dirt or grass strip are in constant use and some airplanes have never known any other kind of home.

The letter "X" indicates an airport or runway that has been closed. These are included on the map for purposes of

navigation, and because they might suffice in an emergency. The southwestern states have many such abandoned airports; often reflecting old military training fields.

The center column in the section under Aerodrome Data gives a characteristic list of airport data, with the descriptive material in the right and left columns. This is self-explanatory and the format will quickly be committed to memory after planning a few flights. The symbols "U-1" or "U-2" are important to the flying companion. They usually mean that there is a Fixed Base Operator on the field who will be happy to help you "get organized" after landing. This dear friend is discussed at length in other parts of this book.

In the paragraph on Radio Aids to Navigation and Communication Boxes be sure that you note the difference in shape of the VOR, and VORTAC symbols. On the map itself these are found in the center of the large circles with compass headings—the bare bones of the "compass rose." For the aircraft with a DME (Distance Measuring Equipment), only the VORTAC or VOR-DME will allow use of this instrument. The magenta circle with a burst of dots is another radio aid, and signifies the presence of a low frequency beacon at that site. You will note a magenta number close to such a symbol. This is the frequency an ADF (Automatic Direction Finder) will tune for homing information to that navigation aid. Morse Code identification is also seen near the symbol for the radiobeacon and accuracy in tuning is confirmed by hearing the proper Morse Code signal. Review the various boxes which contain information on radio frequencies. The pilot will wish to know what Flight Service Station (FSS) is in his vicinity when he desires weather or en route information. You can be helpful by finding the closest FSS and noting the frequency he should use to call for assistance.

The Sectional Chart

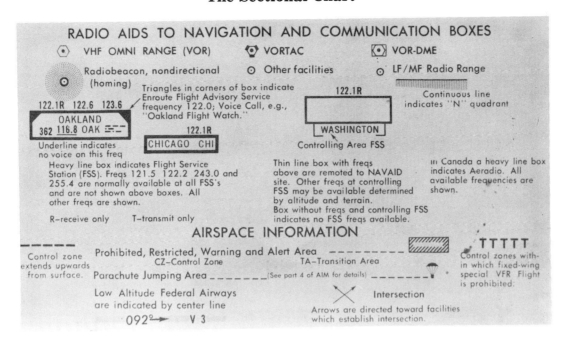

The face of the Sectional Chart also defines the various radio aids to navigation, as well as communication and airspace information. A few minutes careful study and an occasional quick reference to this portion of the Sectional Chart will solve a host of problems in chart interpretation.

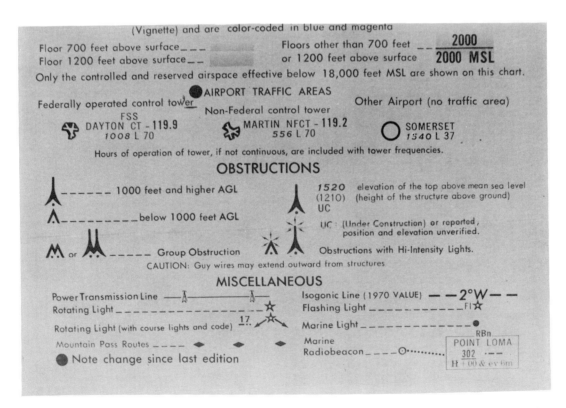

On a hazy day, nothing is more important than information about obstructions to aerial navigation. Remember that the ticked lines showing "boxes of terrain" with their central numbers, i.e. 4⁷, refer to natural terrain features. The man-made obstructions exceed these figures and an understanding of this point will allow correct calculations of obstruction and terrain clearance.

From White Knuckles to Cockpit Cool

The material on Airspace Information contains several points of importance to the novice flight planner. There should be no question in your mind about the information concerning Prohibited, Restricted, Warning and Alert Areas. Open the map and be certain that these shadowed lines are seen and understood. No flight should be planned across such areas without consulting the descriptive material aligned along the edge of the open map. The small parachute symbol should be noted and if that appears along the route of a planned flight, contact with the Flight Service Station by telephone or radio will outline the hours when jumps are scheduled. The author can speak from unhappy experience when she relates that the absence of such a symbol does not mean that parachute jumping will not occur. As a novice pilot she failed to check NOTAMS on a cross country flight and suddenly was in the midst of a group of descending jumpers near Yuma. This resulted in the embarrassment of a landing and explanation of her sins to the officials of the Federal Aviation Administration in the FSS at Yuma.

The third piece of very important information to the flight planner is the diagram of a Low Altitude Federal Airway, with the number 092 degrees followed by an arrow, and the number V 3 in sequence. The 092 indicates the magnetic heading and the arrow the direction of the airway. This simplifies flight planning and prevents an error from creeping into the directional calculations if figured on the plotter. The subsequent V 3 indicates the number of the Airway and its use is described in the chapter on Filing the Flight Plan.

Obstructions are shown by symbols, with a triangle shape for those rising less than 1000 feet above ground level, and a pylon appearance for the really tall towers reaching heights of more than 1000 feet above terrain. The numbers seen at the side of each such obstruction are in heavy type to list the elevation above sea level, and in light type and surrounded by parenthesis marks to indicate the height above ground level.

Miscellaneous markings are far more diverse than listed, and it will take study, imagination, and the help of a skilled pilot to immediately comprehend all of the symbols found on a Sectional chart. Most are descriptive, such as ovals for race tracks, pickaxes for mines, flags for golf courses, pylons connected by lines for power transmission lines, flat blue surfaces for bodies of water often showing a black line at one end at the site of a dam. Your eye will quickly identify salt flats, small symbols conforming to the shape of

The Sectional Chart is laden with information. The wildlife refuge is seen to the right, with the line enclosing a series of dots. The 4⁷ indicates that within the ticked lines there are no natural obstacles exceeding 4700 feet. Two Restricted Zones are identified. Eight airports of almost every type are included. Race-track ovals, mines, cities, freeways, railroads, an OMNI, a drag strip, a power plant, and a whole legion of terrain information is included in this small segment of chart—one which a general aviation airplane might fly over in 5-15 minutes.

Two very important features are depicted in this portion of the Sectional Chart. A Restricted Zone over the Salton Sea is defined. Recall that on the edge of the Sectional Chart will be found information related to each individual Restricted Zone. In many instances the restrictions are minor and limited only to portions of the day or week, or may relate only to specific altitudes. South and west of R-2521 is an area outlined by a solid line with a series of dots interior to the line. This is a wildlife refuge and for reasons of ecology, low flight over such areas is discouraged.

an outdoor theater, oil tanks, freeways, and railroads.

A good exercise at this point it to open the chart at random, pick four of the oblong boxes made up of latitudinal and longitudinal ticked lines. See if you can explain every number and symbol you see in this test area. If you can, you are certainly ready for flight planning. While doing this you should also carefully study the contour lines so that you have the "feel" of the terrain configuration and "see" the flat map in third dimension.

The Sectional Chart has other aids to flight planning. Complex, populous areas may be treated separately with inset maps using a larger scale and "blown up" for ease of pilotage. Along the lower edge of the map are three scales showing kilometers, statute miles, and nautical miles allowing for rapid conversions. The material on prohibited, restricted, warning, and alert areas has been described

in earlier paragraphs. A list of control tower frequencies, with the hours of operation and the ATIS frequencies forms a column on the chart. Regulations pertinent to aircraft by the National Park Service, Fish and Wildlife Service, and National Forest and Wilderness Area are also briefly described.

You next will be planning a flight and preparing to help the pilot file the resultant flight plan. This should be an easy exercise after your comprehensive study of the Sectional Chart. More than this, however, the information gleaned will allow you to quickly orient yourself from the air on your next actual flight. The best insurance against an emergency is preparedness, and should that unlikely call come from the pilot to "find me the closest airport," you will be located on the Sectional and ready to direct him to a safe landing.

4

THE VOR,
THE COMPASS ROSE,
AND
MAGNETIC VS. TRUE NORTH

The above ingredients must be discussed together because they relate so directly with each other. Let us begin with the "compass rose." The term derives from some very ornate drawings of the compass points which fancifully resemble the petals of a rose. On your Sectional Chart only the "bare bones" remain, but the term persists. Do you see the many circles with numbers marking the periphery? On most you will find numbers in increments of thirty, hence 0, 30, 60, 90, etc. Five degree interval marks appear, although on many there will be some markings and numbers omitted. In a few instances in very congested areas the entire circle may be absent, and only the center designated with the appropriate box of information at the side.

The center circle is present if there is simply a VOR, and a squared triangle if the navigation aid is a VORTAC, meaning that it has Tacan capability. Either of these identifying marks locates the exact position of the most widely used navigation aid in the United States. This is a Very High Frequency Omnidirectional Range; the acronym for which is VOR. When seen from the air, the building in which the VOR is housed appears to be a large white plate with a central knob-like handle. When visited on the ground, it looks like a large white bowling pin sitting on a plate, with the plate sitting in turn on a small housing structure. Inside this odd looking building is a station which projects VHF radio signals, or "radials" for each of the 360 degrees of the compass.

The VOR, the Compass Rose, and Magnetic Vs. True North

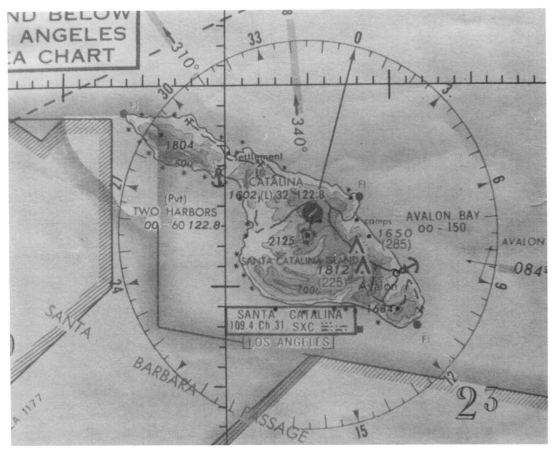

The "compass rose" as it appears on the Los Angeles Chart on Santa Catalina. The VORTAC is the center of the rose. The number "0" appears in the "true north" positon.

The jet looks as if it is going to bowl over the VOR or OMNI housing sitting next to this Hawaiian runway. In heavy weather this "tenpin-like" structure would have beamed the signals to bring the jet directly to the airport.

From White Knuckles to Cockpit Cool

It is to be remembered that these are magnetic bearings and if you are looking at "magnetic north" rather than "true north" you will be facing the 0 degree radial of the VOR. This term, incidentally, is used interchangeably with OMNI.

We should now briefly consider "magnetic north" and "true north". For those who have dealt little with compass headings such terms may initially seem confusing. Think in these terms: the mass of metallic magnetic material which attracts the compass needle happens fortuitously to be located reasonably near the true North Pole. At the real North Pole there is nothing to deflect the compass, but navigators through centuries have benefited from the proximity of these "two poles." By adding or subtract-

ting the difference between magnetic and true north we are able to steer accurately with the magnetic compass.

For the purpose of this book we will explain a simple short cut involving a "slide over" method for determining the heading of your flight. This is described in the subsequent chapter on the Practice Flight Plan, and uses the compass rose on the Sectional Chart and the plotter to give reasonably accurate magnetic headings. Once you have become more experienced in flight planning, you may want to enroll in a ground school and become intimately acquainted with "magnetic lines of variation" and the actual calculations made by your pilot of true vs. magnetic north, course vs. heading, using other capabilities of your maps and plotter.

THE PRACTICE FLIGHT PLAN

Your pilot will be accustomed to preparing his flight plan, but you will be a much more interested and helpful flying companion if you participate in this phase of the preparation for a trip. This chapter will allow you to actually prepare a flight plan over a relatively simple route, going through the same motions you would use in a long cross-country trip. As discussed in "Tools the Pilot Uses," you will need **current** Sectional Charts for the areas you plan to cover, a **current** airport guide, your plotter and computer, a flight plan form, and for your use, this book. While not absolutely necessary, planning will be easier and more complete if you can obtain current IFR charts and approach plates for airports that might serve as landing fields on your proposed flight. The Fixed Base Operator will have the majority of this equipment, although he may not have available IFR charts or approach plates. Experienced commercial pilots will probably have these in their flight bags,

and you should query your pilot friends and photocopy any material that is not readily purchased. Should the FBO not have some of the major items listed, they may be ordered from aircraft supply houses listed in the appendix of this book.

For practice you will now plan a flight using the Los Angeles Sectional Chart. Your planned route will take you from Montgomery Field in San Diego to Hemet-Ryan Airport near the small city of Hemet. This will be a "direct" route and will not involve the use of a Victor airway as no such designated route connects these two cities.

Begin by placing your plotter in the center of the symbol indicating Montgomery Field. Using it as a straight-edge, draw a line directly from this point to the shoreline to the west, where a triangle with a dot at its base and the number 1049 are seen. Next, draw a line from this point on the shoreline directly to the center of Hemet-Ryan Airport to the north. Draw several arrows on these

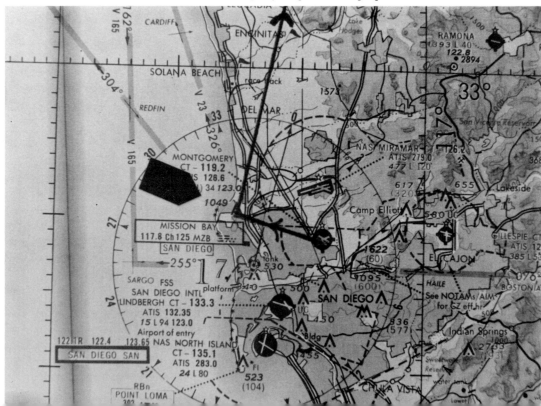

PILOT'S PREFLIGHT CHECK LIST

DATE

WEATHER ADVISORIES	ALTERNATE WEATHER	NOTAMS
EN ROUTE WEATHER	FORECASTS	AIRSPACE RESTRICTIONS
DESTINATION WEATHER	WINDS ALOFT	MAPS

FLIGHT LOG

DEPARTURE POINT	VOR	RADIAL	DISTANCE		TIME	
	IDENT.	TO	LEG	PT-TO-PT / CUMULATIVE	TAKEOFF	GROUND SPEED
	FREQ.	FROM	REMAINING			
CHECK POINT					ETA	
					ATA	
DESTINATION						
			TOTAL			

POSITION REPORT: FVFR report hourly, IFR as required by ATC

ACFT. IDENT.	POSITION	TIME	ALT.	IFR/VFR	EST. NEXT FIX	NAME OF SUCCEEDING FIX	PIREPS

REPORT CONDITIONS ALOFT—
CLOUD TOPS, BASES, LAYERS, VISIBILITY, TURBULENCE, HAZE, ICE, THUNDERSTORMS

This represents the "informal" side of the Flight Plan form, and is one of the many ways that a Flight Log can be handled. For long flights under VFR conditions there is clearly inadequate space for check-point information, and each pilot develops his own form of Flight Log.

lines pointing in the direction of your route of flight. This will prove important when you are actually in the cockpit following your planned flight. Holding the chart in the direction of flight is surprisingly valuable. Much confusion will evaporate through the simple technique of orienting your route of flight as drawn on the map, in the direction of the nose of the airplane. As in any other map, the top of the chart is north, but since you will not always be flying north, the chart should be rotated. You will find that this is much easier than mentally moving a river or mountain.

At this juncture you must determine the course on the compass you will fly to reach Hemet-Ryan. For purposes of simplicity you will use a "short-cut" method which is reasonably accurate. As you get farther into this "flying business" and your understanding of the plotter increases, a more accurate technique can be used. The simple device is to again use the plotter as a straight-edge. Align it carefully along the first leg of your route. Now slide the plotter down to the center

Your very first check point is Mt. Soledad and the tower noted by the proper obstruction symbol. The shoreline is an added assurance that you have begun your plan in the proper direction.

The Practice Flight Plan

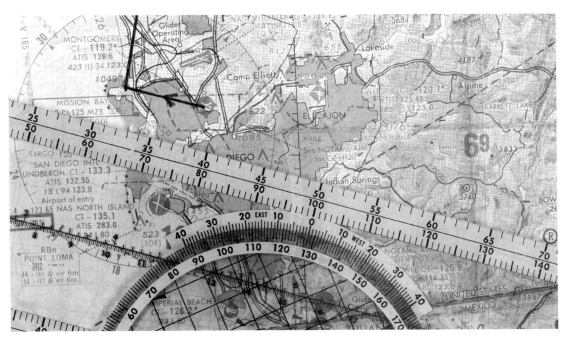

This demonstrates the "slide over" technique using the compass "rose" to determine your initial magnetic heading. As you can identify, the plotter—parallel with your course line—crosses the compass "rose" at about 273 degrees. This is a magnetic heading.

* * *

The "slide over" technique identifies the magnetic heading of the second "leg" of your flight to Hemet-Ryan, and approximates 358 degrees.

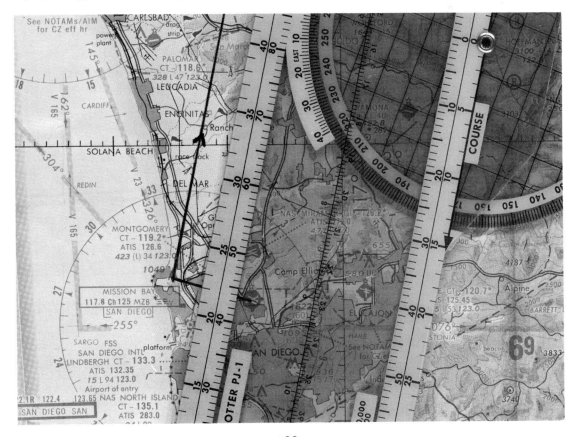

of the Mission Bay (San Diego) compass rose, maintaining the exact angle you have determined. The compass rose encircles the San Diego VOR and is slightly to the left and below your marked course. Read the number corresponding to your line of flight, and you will see that it is a magnetic course of approximately 273 degrees. This figure should be entered on your flight plan. Next, you should align the edge of the plotter on the line from the point where you have crossed the shore to the center of the symbol for the Hemet-Ryan Airport. Slide your plotter carefully to the right to the center of the circle, maintaining the proper angle. The line indicates a course of about 358 degrees, almost exactly magnetic north.

It is now necessary to determine the altitude you will fly to clear all obstacles. Look at the large numbers in the center of the oblong boxes formed by the latitudinal and longitudinal lines. None of the terrain in this large area exceed 4700 feet. On your particular line of flight the tallest obstruction on the course is

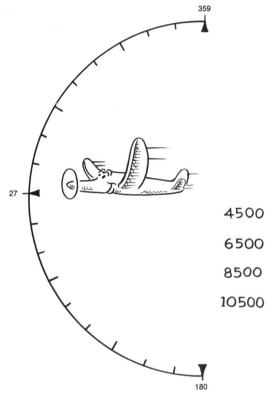

4500
6500
8500
10500

2555 feet. A rule of thumb is to fly at least 1000 feet above the tallest obstruction. This would mean that a safe altitude would exceed 3555 feet. In addition to your scrutiny of the line of flight for terrain and man-made obstructions, you should check the color column on the face sheet of the Sectional Chart to reconfirm the fact that there is no higher ground than you have noted. Look carefully along the course line to see if a black dot followed by a number exceeds your planned minimum altitude.

When you are triply secure in your choice of altitude for the flight you must correlate this with the rules governing traffic separation. When flying in excess of 3000 feet above the ground under Visual Flight Rules (VFR) a flight path from 0 degrees to 179 degrees must fly on odd thousands plus 500 feet, i.e. 3500, 5500, 7500, etc. A course line from 180 degrees to 359 degrees flies on even thousands plus 500 feet, i.e. 4500, 6500, 8500, etc. Under Instrument Flight Rules (IFR), this same technique is used, but

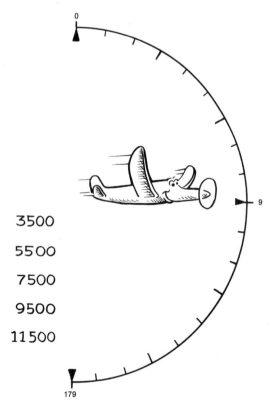

3500
5500
7500
9500
11500

The edge of the plotter measures the distance in nautical miles from Montgomery Field to the shore-line.

the flight is on the thousand, rather than the thousand plus 500 number. It is reassuring to know that a separation of 500 feet is maintained en route, although it is also obvious that during a climb or a descent these altitudes are invaded and that at least one pair of eyes should be "outside of the cockpit" at all times. It is also appropriate to mention that although the pilot can fly safely to 3000 feet above ground level or below, there is a safety advantage at the higher elevations where traffic separation is enforced.

Since you now know that your direction of flight falls within the 180 to 359 degree magnetic heading, and that you must fly at an altitude at or above 3555 feet, your altitude selection can be 4500 feet. This should be entered on your flight plan. During the flight your pilot may elect to climb to 6500 or 8500 feet in order to be more comfortable or to improve visibility, but since such climbs are costly in both time and fuel the flight plan should reflect the best possible conditions. Since your course is so near to magnetic north and the point where altitude separation rules change, more than the usual vigilance for other aircraft is needed.

Next, take your plotter and turn it to the "Sectional" scale. In this flight plan **nautical** rather than **statute** miles will be used, and you should be absolutely certain that you have the right scale and that you are consistent in its use throughout the subsequent measurements. Place the "0" of the nautical side in the center of the symbol for Montgomery Field and read the number of nautical miles to the shoreline. It reads seven miles, and a measurement from the shoreline at the 1049 number to Hemet-Ryan Airport adds 55 more nautical miles. This is a flight of 62 nautical miles, and should be entered as the "total" on your Flight Log.

Remove the plotter and look along the course line for possible "check points." These will be easily identifiable features of terrain or man-made objects that can be easily seen from an aircraft in flight, and will orient you along your route. Freeways, bodies of water, dams, peaks, airports, towns, racetracks, drive-in theaters, and manufacturing plants with smokestacks make excellent reference points. For best visibility a check point should be five to ten nautical miles on either side of the course line at usual cruising altitudes. Remember that "straight down" objects are hard to see from many airplanes and objects are much more easily identified off to the side. Each chosen check point should be measured for distance from the course line. These should now be entered on your Flight Log.

The first excellent check point is the shoreline with Miramar Naval Air Station and its long runways off the right wing as you turn to the north. Place your plotter at right angles to the course line and draw a line one-half inch long when your turn has drawn you even with Miramar. Although this is only three miles from your change in heading to the north, there is an airport traffic area for Miramar and your pilot must gain adequate altitude before he crosses this area. This relatively slow climb will allow you time to orient yourself and find other identifiable points such as Lindbergh

The flight from Montgomery Field to Hemet-Ryan takes into consideration the proximity of Miramar Naval Air Station, a very active military jet training station. The flight is directed to the shore-line to avoid the necessity of crossing directly over Miramar.

Field to the south and the two major freeways to the east and west of Miramar Naval Air Station.

To your right, ten nautical miles east of Miramar is San Vicente Reservoir. This is 15 nautical miles from your planned route and is somewhat distant to be a first class check point, but such a large body of water is usually easy to see and the configuration with a dam at the southern end and an island in the middle makes it an acceptable landmark.

The freeway roughly paralleling your course of flight, and six miles to your right, is an excellent continuing reference. If, during your flying career you hear an obviously novice pilot jokingly tell you that he came in IFR, he may really be indicating that for him IFR means "I fly roads."

A large and busy freeway, and San Vicente Reservoir are next in sight. The coast-line is beginning to drift away to the left, and the route moves inland.

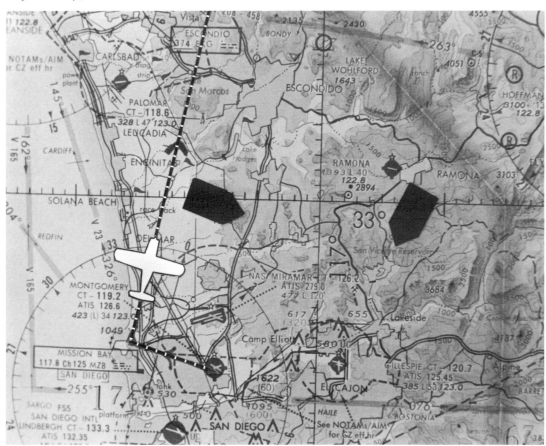

The Practice Flight Plan

On your right is a peak with a black dot and the number 1573. This might seem to be a good check point, but with experience and appreciation of contour lines you will realize that this is not a peak of sufficient height to be seen clearly.

Lake Hodges is a good reference point and lies to the right of your course line. The dam at the southern end of the lake is at mile 13 from your turn north. Confirmation of this check point can be made readily by the freeway farther to the right, the city of Ramona with its airport on the western side 15 miles to your right, and the city of Escondido ahead and to the right. Palomar Airport should be visible ahead and to the left.

At Escondido the freeway cuts under the route of flight and appears again to the left. To the right, or east of your course and about 15 nautical miles ahead, some peaks reaching 5000-6000 feet will appear. These are valuable as long range check points.

Just to the right of your path of flight is a small airport with an "R" in the open circle. Although this might seem to be a good check point, it probably would be difficult to see as it has a dirt runway as the open circle signifies, and there are no identifying topographical features nearby.

Contour lines and the color of the map tell you that Pauma Valley Airport to the

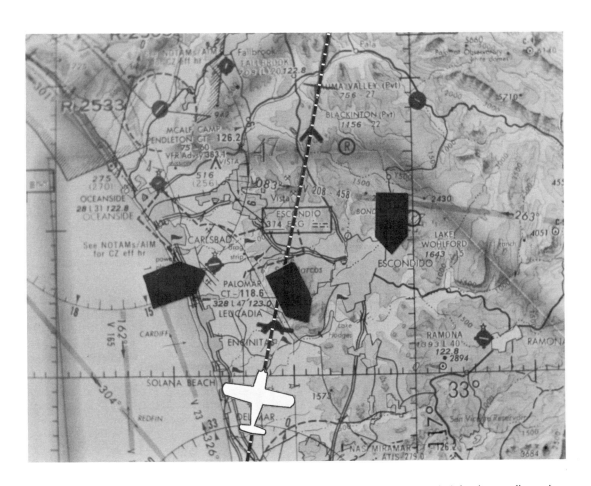

Unless obscured by clouds or haze, Lake Hodges should be clearly identified by its configuration. Palomar Airport on the left sits on the top of a small mesa and is usually easy to spot. In fact, the proximity of your course to Hemet-Ryan takes you relatively close to Palomar Airport and special attention should be given to planes making their downwind or crosswind approach.

right of the course line at mile 30 is located in a broad valley. This airport is about the correct distance to the right of your line of flight to make a good check point and should be easy to identify. Looking to the left of the course another airport is visible. This is Fallbrook Airport and spotting it in flight will reassure you that you have not invaded the restricted zone which it borders. For practice the restricted zones designated R-2503 and R-2533 should be viewed and the specifics relating to these zones checked by reading the descriptive material on the margin of the Sectional Chart.

At the small town of Pala to your right a large road passes beneath your line of flight making an "X" configuration with the north-south highway. Farther to the right the map shows an area of odd markings in a mountainous area. The key to the chart will show that this is a wildlife refuge and should be avoided. The reasons are multiple. The contour lines tell that this is rugged country. No roads penetrate the mountains and an emergency landing would be difficult. Since it is a refuge, the clatter of airplane engines should be avoided.

Race track ovals are usually readily visible. At Rancho California there are tracks both to the right and left of the course line. There is also a small body of water east of the race track on the right of your course. The dam at this reservoir is at the west end as you can see by the oblique black line. On the left to the west of the course, there is an airport contiguous to the other race track. The prominent Lake Elsinore can be seen in the distance to the west. Your check point in this region should be even with the dam on the right and the Rancho California Airport on the left. This will be at mile forty.

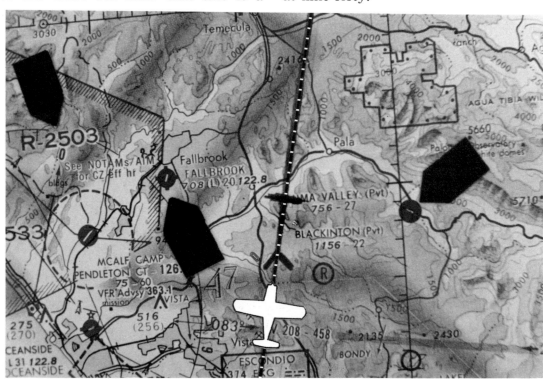

Fallbrook and Pauma Valley airports lie next along your course. Be sure to heed the Restricted Zone, R-2503—as you would not be pleased to have an aircraft from Camp Pendleton escort you to an airport to explain how you happened to fly over their ammunition depot. The area surrounded by a solid line plus dots indicates the boundary of National Park Service areas, U. S. Fish and Wildlife Service areas and U. S. Forest Service Wilderness and Primitive areas.

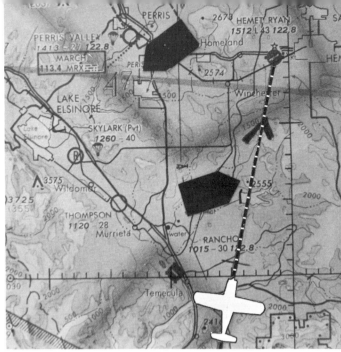

Directly ahead you will distinguish another large body of water with a dam at the west end. You will also see a black dot and the number 2555 on the chart signifying a small peak. Draw your next check point over the second finger of the reservoir at mile forty six. At this juncture Lake Elsinore will be clearly visible off of your left wing. Near Lake Elsinore you will see a small parachute symbol indicating a site for parachute jumping. Make a note on your Flight Log to have the pilot check the NOTAMS about hours of scheduled jumps in this vicinity.

If your planning has been accurate you should see Hemet-Ryan Airport at about this time. Notice the southwest location in relation to the city of Hemet, with rising ground to the west. A road is located just north of the airport.

This exercise shows how detailed, but also how simple flight planning should be. An interstate cross-country flight is no more difficult.

At the base of the photograph you may see the top portion of the wildlife refuge area. The parachute symbol near Perris reveals the possibility that parachute jumpers may be in the vicinity. A call to the Flight Service Station or prior consultation with NOTAMS may give information about this important point.

* * *

As you approach your destination a large number of obvious check points will be evident. Lake Elsinore to the left is a large body of water and will reflect the afternoon sunlight. Hemet-Ryan Airport, just to the left of the city of Hemet, and south of a large freeway, will probably be in clear view.

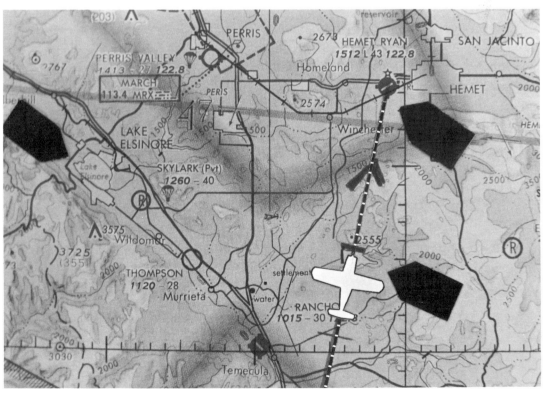

6

LOADING
THE
AIRPLANE

A convenient birthday or Christmas is a great time to begin your preparations for properly loading an airplane. The request list for your Santa should include a suitcase and make-up kit of waterproof nylon and a sportsman's scales which will register up to fifty pounds.

Make it "your thing" to be prepared to tramp across rough terrain or catch a Las Vegas show. Everyone has a packing problem. Mine is shoes. Since my feet need to be babied with frequent changes of heel heights, it is necessary to choose light weight shoes because I must carry a number of pairs. After consideration of any personal problems, try to coordinate colors, uses and weight. Any magazine article telling you how to live a month in Europe with only a plastic "baggie" for luggage should be devoured, digested and translated into a flurry of activity. Depending, of course, on the type of plane

you fly and the number of "souls on board" (it has always bothered me that this is the expression often used in flight plans), you may be able to expand your possessions.

Are you a rock collector? Change to postcards! These are more easily transported on a return trip. Unless you wish to contribute to Uncle Sam's postal service, remember that you must not overload the plane at your original point of departure should you plan any shopping at your destination.

The manufacturer's "gross weight" is not something he dreamed. It is a carefully calculated figure which allows the pilot the greatest possible payload with an adequate margin of safety. Since every flight is not through perfectly smooth air (gross understatement), and sometimes there are short fields and bumpy landings (back to the "touch and go's"), it makes

good sense to stay well within the allowable gross weight.

Calculating this figure is not an exercise in math as it is clearly written in the airplane **Flight Manual.** This manual must, by law, be carried in the plane and the manual in your plane applies specifically to your aircraft alone. So, to begin the loading of the plane we start by setting down the weights of all items to be carried. The total weight of the plane, the people, the luggage, and the gas and oil (yes, they must be countcd) must never exceed the gross weight allowed for your aircraft.

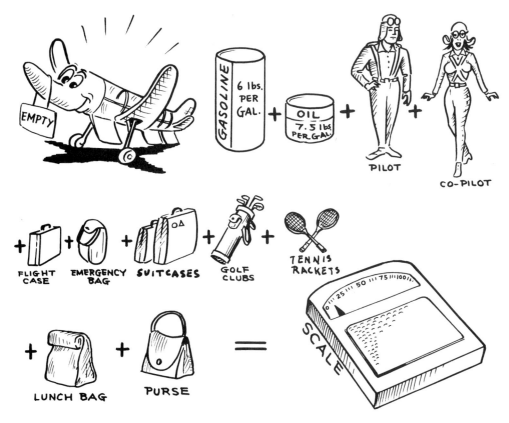

From White Knuckles to Cockpit Cool

The next important consideration in loading is the balance of the airplane. To visualize this, think of the airplane as a child's teeter-totter. The center of gravity of the teeter-totter is the supporting pole in the center. The center of gravity (C.G.) of the airplane is a point in the plane at which you can consider all the weight to be located. This is a point that has been fixed by the design and location of the equipment in the plane. Just as two children of equal weights will balance a teeter-totter so that the plank will remain horizontal, equal distribution of weight in a plane will keep it balanced. However, if you put Fat Jimmy on one end and Skinny Sal on the other, one end will go up and the other down. The same is true of an airplane. Too many heavy items forward of the C.G. will cause the craft to be "nose heavy" and too much weight at the rear of the C.G. will result in a "tail heavy" aircraft. Listed in the **Flight Manual** will be the amount of weight

that may be placed in each area. There are also placards on all baggage compartments giving the **maximum** weight that may be placed in that area under the most ideal of circumstances. This is a **"never exceed"** number!!! The manufacturer has calculated safe forward and aft limits for the C.G. at various aircraft weights and it is essential that the loading be kept within these limits. When you hear the term "within the envelope," it means that the load and distribution of the load are safe and correct.

With the information that you have now gathered: the basic empty weight of the airplane, the weight of the usable fuel (multiply six pounds per gallon of gasoline), the weight of the oil (multiply 7.5 pounds per gallon—not quart), the weight of each passenger, the weight of each piece of baggage; you are now ready to compute the "weight and balance" to ensure that you do stay "within the envelope." Once this is completed and

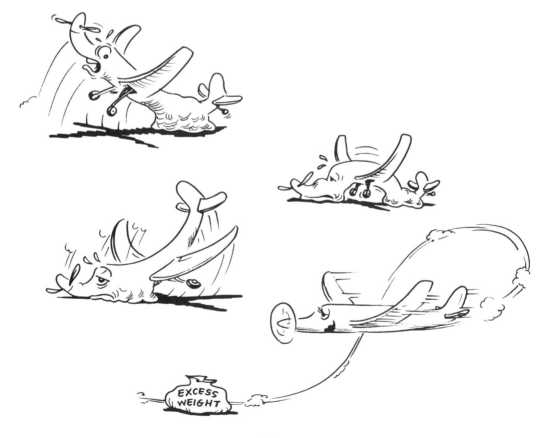

Loading the Airplane

checked with the pilot, actual packing can proceed. It might be noted that there are convenient devices for most aircraft that compute the weight and balance without any arithmetic. These are inexpensive and highly recommended. They do not obviate the necessity to do accurate weighing. They merely make the calculations for you, just like a panty hose package indicates your proper size.

In "theory" loading the plane is the responsibility of the pilot, but in practice this is another aspect of the flight where the duties can be shared or, with experience, can be completely assumed.

One final word concerning this important aspect of flying. Do cinch everything down with the straps or nets that are provided in the baggage areas. If your plane has a forward baggage compartment be sure that there are no metal objects that might affect instrument function or bounce into the instrument area during rough flight.

When you master proper loading of the aircraft and understand weight and balance, you will have learned skills that will be invaluable to the pilot and make you a much more efficient flying companion.

Staying "within the envelope" of weight and aircraft balance means accurate weighing of every item placed in the aircraft. Compartments are usually placarded as to maximum weights and these must be heeded.

7

CHECK!

THE
WALK AROUND

Finished packing the plane? This is a good time to do a "walk around." While this is actually the responsibility of the pilot, there can never by too many checks for safety. It is the lack of pre-flight planning activities that causes many emergencies. The walk around is a complete and routinized visual inspection of certain specific parts of the airplane as well as inspection of the plane as a whole.

In the airplane as in cooking it is extremely important to establish a fixed routine. Anyone who can learn to juggle assembly, cooking and serving of an entire meal can certainly learn to spot a variation from the normal in one airplane!

The word "normal" is the important key in a walk around. It is necessary to learn what is normal for your airplane and to call to the attention of the pilot anything in your check list that varies from the usual. If any of the terms used in this chapter are unfamiliar, refer to the

"Glossary of Terms" found at the back of the book.

Begin your inspection with the same part of the aircraft and proceed in the same order each time. Every plane has similar places that must be checked out but each plane has its own variations. Do not permit questions of other passengers or passers-by to interrupt this routine. Indeed, it is an excellent idea to perform your inspection when you are completely alone and unhurried. A check of an Aztec with which the authors are most familiar begins in the cabin where oxygen supplies are checked; the windshield is checked for cleanliness; the cowl flap position is viewed; a check is made to be sure that the Master switch is off, and the yoke is loosened by slipping off the seat belt used to hold it in a fixed position. When tied this immobilizes the ailerons and elevator preventing their flailing in a high wind. Loosening the yoke allows freedom of movement of the horizontal surfaces and

The Walk Around

A clean windshield makes all the difference when flying "into the morning or evening sun." It also facilitates avoidance of other aircraft, and helps in penetrating smoke or haze during a landing.

the ailerons so that inspection can be completed.

Completion of the cabin inspection leads to a check of the right wing and includes a visual inspection of the wing surfaces top and bottom to ascertain if any dents or scratches have appeared since the last flight. The wing light should be touched and viewed to make sure that it is secure. We have had the experience of a broken wing light during an overnight stop. Next, an inspection of the aileron top and bottom to see if any bolts or screws on the arms holding it do not appear tight. Check the counter-weight to be sure that it moves freely. This inspection requires peering into some dark recesses. Gasoline caps in the right wing should be removed, inspected, and the gasoline level confirmed by inserting a finger into the tank or directly viewing the level of fuel. The caps should then be replaced and secured in the proper fashion. The fact that you supervised the filling of the airplane with fuel the preceding night should not be taken as a guarantee that everything in this department is secure and ready. Gasoline may leak or, in these days of extremely high fuel prices, may be siphoned from tanks. This gasoline check is an extremely important part of the walk around. It is wise to be aware of the overflow provision in your airplane's fuel system. This avoids a moment of panic when you feel that there is a leak in the fuel tanks by virtue of spilled fuel on the cement. Like almost all fluids, gasoline expands with heat, and tanks filled in the cool of the night may overflow slightly as the sun heats the wings.

Progress to the right engine if your plane is a twin. Look into the front of the cowling and check for loose parts, and

Be absolutely certain that the gasoline caps are firmly seated, or the Bernoulli effect of the air rushing past an open tank will result in siphoning of gasoline at an alarming rate!

foreign objects such as birds' nests! Yes, this can be a problem in some areas on even a short stop. As much of the engine as can be viewed comfortably should be checked. Run both eyes and fingers along the edge of the right propeller to check for nicks or cracks. Be sure to call these to the

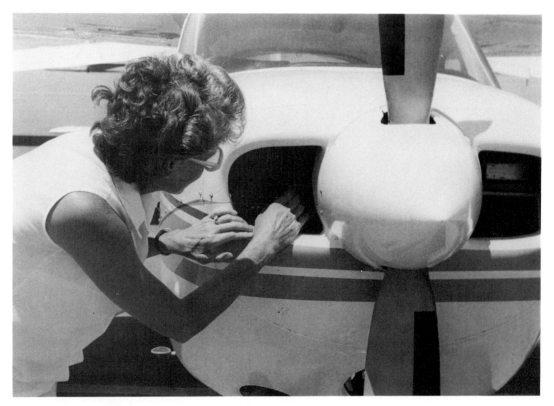

In the "Spring a young man's fancy may turn to thoughts of love," and that is true of birds who may build the start of a nest in a convenient aperture. Look before you fly!

Propeller nicks and cracks are important to find and correct. This is true at any point on the propeller, but particularly along the "leading edge," and near the tip where the rate of speed is tremendous.

attention of the pilot. Nicks should be filed by a mechanic, as the vibration caused by the whirling propeller can result in cracks and decreased performance. The nose cone should also be inspected for cracks or insecure fittings.

At this point the right wheel should be checked. The tire should have good tread and there should be no unusual wear on the sides. In aircraft with retractable gear this might signify improper seating of the wheel in the wheel-well. Check all lines leading to the wheel to be sure that all lines are secure and no fluid is leaking. Look at the cowl flap to verify the position noted on the cowl flap indicator in the cabin.

The oil dipstick should be examined to measure the amount and condition of the engine oil. If it is dirty it might be good to check the engine log to see when it was last changed and notify your pilot. Replace the dipstick and check the security of its seating.

In a twin you would then proceed to the nose and check the landing light, taxi light, nose wheel tire, front wheel-well, and all of the lines leading to it. If the gear is of the oleo type, proper extension should be checked on all wheels. Next comes the left engine, left wheel, and left wing. In the case of the Aztec as well as other aircraft the left wing will have a stall warning indicator that should be ac-

The oil "dipstick" may be hot and may dirty your manicure, but better that than a "frozen" engine ruined by lack of oil! After the inspection, be sure that the dipstick is fully seated, or an oil spray may occur as a result of siphonage.

Pitot tube covers are large and flashy for obvious reasons! Among other problems the pilot would have no idea of his airspeed with a pitot cover in place.

tuated to be sure that it moves freely. If the wing "fails to fly" because of an excessive angle of attack this indicator will activate a buzzer and a warning light in the cockpit indicating that a stall is near. You will probably never hear this warning except in rare cases during landing when it may be perfectly normal. The pitot tube is also located under the left wing of the Aztec and should be carefully inspected to be sure that, if a cover is used, it has been removed, and that no foreign substances such as dirt or bugs are lodged in the two holes that make up the pitot-

static system. Some of the major flight instruments will not operate accurately unless these apertures are free and open.

The gasoline draining device for our plane is stowed in a holder in the forward baggage compartment. The fuel sumps are on the lower, inner aspect of each engine, protected by a small panel. It is important to use a clear cylinder of some type so that gasoline drained from each of the fuel lines can be viewed carefully. It is not a good idea to drain the gasoline directly onto the runway. It is impossible to check carefully for dirt, water or sedi-

The pitot-static system is responsible for several important instruments, and the pitot tube must be clean and open. If a pitot tube cover has been used, it obviously must be removed before flight.

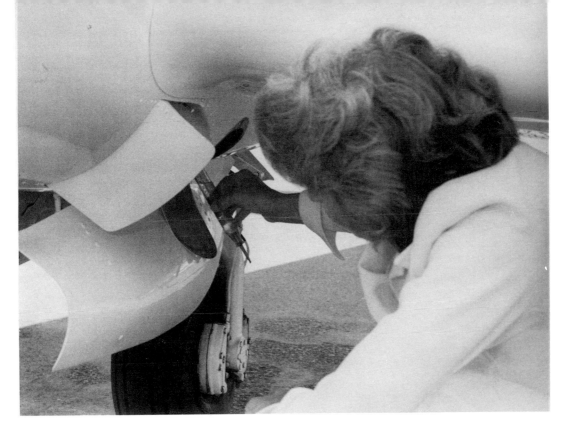

Sediment and water in the gasoline are deadly enemies to engine function. Sumps are provided and should be drained prior to every flight! Even if the stop is merely for fuel, the sumps should be checked.

ment if you cannot hold up the cylinder to look directly at the fuel. If water is present it will be very evident in the bottom of the container. Water and gasoline do not mix. To be aware of what is abnormal, put some water into the bottom of the container and then fill it with gasoline. Their separation is distinct and never again will you worry about your ability to spot water in the fuel! If you observe either water or sediment, drain as many containers as necessary to obtain totally clear gasoline. Tell the pilot of your findings!!! Return the drainage cylinder to its place and check the front compartment to be sure that all baggage is secure and that there are no loose objects that could fly into the instrument area. Be sure that there are no obviously loose wires.

Walk to the rear of the plane and observe all antennae as well as the strobe light. Inspect the tail and trim tab bolts. Check the freedom of the horizontal tail surface. View the security of the baggage in the rear baggage compartment. In the case of the author's plane it is also possi-

ble at this time to be sure that the oxygen lines are sound and secure, and that the emergency locator beacon and its antennae are in the proper position.

When the pilot has completed his walk around be sure that all baggage compartments are closed and locked.

After the pilot is in the left seat so that he may activate the switches, the bulbs in the rotating beacon, the landing light, the taxi light, and the strobe light can be checked. Wing tip lights may also be viewed with switches on. If there is a central fuel pump, it should be drained by the pilot, and the flying companion can make sure that the valve shutting the drain operates properly and the drain does actually shut.

Nothing should be left to chance or memory. If you learn enough about the plane to do this, it will give you infinitely more confidence and a feeling that you have some control over your destiny. There is also less time to worry about the upcoming flight if you are still a member of the "white knuckles" set!

45

FILING
THE
FLIGHT PLAN

The flight has been planned, the airplane correctly loaded, the walk-around completed, and the weather checked either by telephone to the "pilot's one-call briefing" number listed under "U.S. Government, Department of Transportation," or directly by conversation with the briefer in the Flight Service Station. All systems are "go," and the time has finally arrived to file the flight plan. This is

A weather briefing prior to filing the flight plan is an important part of the filing process. It is not possible to accurately determine your estimated time of arrival without wind and weather information. This may be otained in person at a Flight Service Station, by aviation radio, or as in this instance, by a telephone conversation with the weather briefer.

usually done by telephone to the Flight Service Station but, when feasible, it is instructive to talk to the briefer on a person to person basis at his desk. In this situation the actual sequence reports, weather maps and "prog charts" are available for viewing and explanation by the briefer. NOTAMS can be checked and discussed. Any special problems can be worked out, and the flight plan reviewed by the briefer for accuracy. Under unusual circumstances the plan is filed by radio after the trip has begun, but this is generally done when there has been a change in the weather and the pilot wishes to file under Instrument Flight Rules (IFR). A flight plan filed in the air under Visual Flight Rules (VFR) hints at poor planning, but is certainly better than no flight plan at all.

Flight plans are not mandatory when the weather allows VFR or "special VFR" takeoffs. If the weather is below minimums the flight must be IFR and a flight plan is required. Cautious pilots often file an IFR flight plan on cloudless days. They are more comfortable with the services of a controller monitoring their progress on a radar screen or by frequent radio checks. Under this circumstance the pilot will be warned of approaching traffic, and vectored around areas of high

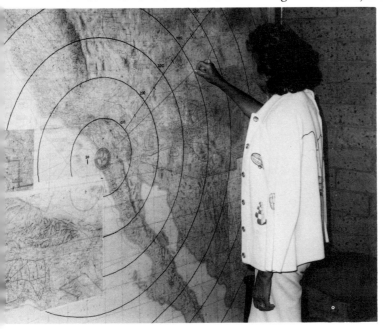

Many Fixed Base Operators supply maps with simple devices to estimate the distance and direction of flight from "Point 'A' to Point 'B'." This presents no substitute for accurate flight planning but gives a general outline of the distance involved and the terrain over which you will fly.

aircraft activity. As he approaches the landing no time is lost finding the airport or being directed into the pattern. Such pilots need an instrument rating for this service to be freely given and this is another inducement for the private pilot to increase his skills by attainment of an instrument ticket.

During daylight hours the flying companion has no difficulty knowing whether the weather is above or below minimums when she first arrives at the airport. If the rotating light on the field is showing alternately green and white, the ceiling and visibility are low enough that instrument flight is necessary.

Both VFR and IFR flight plans are filed on the same printed form (see Flight Plan). We will go through the usual technique of filing and discuss each section of the form. The terms VFR and IFR have been described. DVFR is discussed in the chapter on island flying and

signifies a flight under Defense Visual Flight Rules. This type of plan is filed when an Air Defense Identification Zone (ADIZ) is to be entered and usually means only the addition to the flight plan of the anticipated time of arrival at the ADIZ boundary.

The aircraft identification is simply the "N number" expressed in proper nomenclature, hence N5866Y is described as "November 5866 Yankee." The aircraft type describes the make and model, as "Beech Bonanza." Special equipment alludes to the presence of distance measuring equipment and a transponder. An Aztec with both DME and transponder would be described as "PAZT 23 250 slant A." This tells the briefer that this is an Aztec with 250 horsepower engines and both DME and transponder. The true airspeed is described in knots, and the departure point names the airfield and should include the city, as "Dallas Redbird."

DEPARTMENT OF TRANSPORTATION— FEDERAL AVIATION ADMINISTRATION **FLIGHT PLAN**					Form Approved OMB No. 04-R0072	
. TYPE VFR IFR DVFR	2. AIRCRAFT IDENTIFICATION	3. AIRCRAFT TYPE/ SPECIAL EQUIPMENT	4. TRUE AIRSPEED KTS	5. DEPARTURE POINT	6. DEPARTURE TIME PROPOSED (Z) | ACTUAL (Z)	7. CRUISING ALTITUDE
8. ROUTE OF FLIGHT						
9. DESTINATION (Name of airport and city)	10. EST. TIME ENROUTE HOURS | MINUTES	11. REMARKS				
12. FUEL ON BOARD HOURS | MINUTES	13. ALTERNATE AIRPORT (S)	14. PILOT'S NAME, ADDRESS & TELEPHONE NUMBER & AIRCRAFT HOME BASE				15. NUMBER ABOARD
16. COLOR OF AIRCRAFT	**CLOSE VFR FLIGHT PLAN WITH_____FSS ON ARRIVAL**					

The "official" side of the flight plan form is shown. The controller in the Flight Service Station prefers to go over this form in person, but will take the information by telephone or over the aircraft radio. It is very important that the exact sequence be followed in describing your aircraft and your flight.

Filing the Flight Plan

Only the proposed departure time can be given when the plan is filed. and this must be expressed in Zulu (Greenwich Mean) Time. When in doubt concerning Zulu Time check with the fixed base operator or call the briefer by telephone. Many reception areas where flight plans are filed have two clocks, with one set on local time and the other on Zulu Time.

In VFR flying the cruising altitude when above 3000 feet over terrain, will be on odd thousands plus 500 feet when flying east, and on even thousands plus 500 feet when flying west. IFR traffic is assigned by the Center and when filing an IFR flight plan, your pilot can only request a desired altitude. Traffic separation and proper ground clearance will dictate the level finally assigned.

The route of flight will follow either designated airways or be described as "direct." In the example given in the chapter on planning the flight the route would be simply described as, "San Diego Montgomery, direct Hemet Ryan." On a flight from Ocala, Florida to Ocean Reef, Florida the route of flight would be stated as, "Ocala, Victor 157 La Belle, Victor 97 Miami, Victor 51 Biscayne Bay, direct Ocean Reef." The VFR pilot is declaring this as his route of flight. The IFR pilot is requesting a routing and can expect modification dependent on weather and traffic conditions.

A destination airport and the closest city are given at the end of the description of the route, as "Destination Ocean Reef Airport, Ocean Reef Resort."

The time en route is clearly an estimate and in VFR flying can be an educated guess after estimating the distance, airspeed, and winds aloft. In IFR flying voice contact with the controller will repeatedly update the estimated time of arrival at any navigational fix. The fuel on board must be expressed in hours and minutes. This involves conjecture, but the pilot soon learns the rate of fuel flow at various power settings and can be remarkably accurate.

In VFR flight an alternate airport is not stated although any good planner has this in mind during the preparation for the flight. En route weather may force a change in plans and alternatives need to have been considered. Data concerning the pilot and the home base of the aircraft become important if the flight is delayed or if trouble occurs and search and rescue operations are contemplated. Having information allows representatives of the FAA to call the home airport to check if the flight ended safely and the pilot simply forgot to close his flight plan after landing. Happily, this is usually the case.

The number of passengers aboard and the color of the aircraft are frankly related to search and rescue and must be stated.

The log and checklists on the reverse side of the flight plan form are not a formal part of the plan and are included merely as suggested information collected and noted for safety purposes.

Since the flying companion may have participated extensively in the planning phase of the trip and ideally will be a participant in navigation, she deserves to be included in the actual filing. She certainly should insist that a flight plan be filed; have her pencil and paper ready to copy information during the readback of an IFR flight plan; and remind the VFR pilot of the necessity of opening his flight plan after takeoff and closing it after landing.

9

PIE IN THE SKY

Does the title tell all? No sooner are you safely established on your course than you hear the familiar question: "Did you bring anything to eat?" This is vital "need-to-know" information. It is important to have within easy reach a plastic bag filled with food. Goddess of multiple hands that you are, and never losing your place on the map or taking your eyes off of the "check points," you are required to produce an "easy-to-eat" something that will not end up in the lap of the pilot.

Perhaps it is easier to list some "don'ts" that have been learned to the sorrow of the authors.

Don't buy completely filled milk shake cartons just before you lift off. As your plane gains altitude you will suddenly find yourself in the position of the Sorcerer's Apprentice with milk shake flowing all over the cockpit. Don't open carbonated beverages quickly at altitude or again you will find yourself in a sea of sticky liquid. Remember that there is no easy place to dispose of extra liquid from cans unless you have provided for it. Lemonade or iced tea from a thermos jug

with a plastic liner is a better beverage choice. Don't bring foods with strong odors. The cockpit is small enough and the closeness is exaggerated by onions, garlic, or salami! Cheeses, milk chocolate or other potentially heat-sensitive foods are not for the airplane. Taxi time along a hot runway makes the cabin simulate an oven.

Positive suggestions might include: fruits, non-melt types of candy, peanut butter, hard-boiled eggs, or sandwiches cut into "stuff-in-the-mouth" pieces. Avocados can make delicious snacks and be carried for many days if they are bought with an eye to differences in ripeness. There is a high melting-point chocolate which can be purchased in stores that cater to hikers. This type is excellent to have in the emergency kit as well as the lunch.

Have on hand one of the many types of wash cloth packets. These are helpful not only after eating but very necessary to clean soiled fingers after the "walk around." These cloths do, by the way, become dried inside their little foil bags

over a period of time. Buy small supplies for one trip at a time. Carry plenty of small plastic bags to store the litter. It is amazing how quickly the interior of the plane can take on the appearance of the alley behind the supermarket. A roll of paper towels is also a must for food as well as airplane care.

For obvious reasons the amount of food, and especially liquids consumed should be limited. The intake of children and other "short range" individuals should be monitored. Particularly when travelling with children it may be wise to be prepared for any emergency resulting from too much food or liquid. Here again, plastic containers are valuable.

HAVE ON HAND
1. Correct Sectional Chart.
2. Airport Directory.
3. Approach Plate.
4. Pencil.
5. Radio Frequencies.
6. Field Elevation.
7. Orientation of All Runways.
8. Runway Lengths.
9. Lighting Information.
10. Obstructions Within 10 Nautical Miles From Field.
DIRECTIONS FOR PREPARING LANDING

Read Carefully The Following Gourmet Directions.

RECIPE FOR A LANDING

During your flight planning, the necessary ingredients for assisting with the landing will have been assembled. These include the Sectional Chart, an Airport Directory, Approach Plates, and a pencil. During the planning phase as much unchanging information as possible should be gathered for each airport where a landing is anticipated. Included should be the published radio frequencies for the tower, ground control, approach control, ATIS, as well as the location of the airport, field elevation, orientation of all runways, runway lengths, lighting information, and obstructions within a minimum of 10 nautical miles from the field. With all of this information safely gathered, your mind can be uncluttered as you deal with the changing information that is presented as you near your landing site. Where available, the ATIS (Automatic Terminal Information Service) helps greatly with last minute data. The radio should be tuned to the ATIS frequency about 30 miles from the airport. ATIS is a continuous broadcast at high activity airfields, giving weather data, instrument approach procedures in use, active runways, altimeter setting, and any pertinent Notices to Airmen (NOTAMS). Each broadcast will end with the phrase, "on initial contact inform approach control that you have Information Uniform . . . " or another letter of the alphabet. The pilot then repeats this letter on his initial call to approach control and time is saved as the controller has only to update the pilot in the event of a last minute change.

At this point in the landing procedure, the flying companion becomes a memory bank to supply data to the pilot when requested. In addition she serves as an extra pair of eyes to help locate the airport and

Recipe for a Landing

AN ARTIST'S CONCEPT *of* BEAUTY

A PILOT'S CONCEPT *of* BEAUTY

to scan the skies for other traffic. She may be asked to make radio or transponder changes and she should note and comment on the status of the windsock.

The demands on the pilot as landing nears are heavy. They also vary greatly depending on the weather, traffic, and whether the airport is "controlled," or "uncontrolled." At busy airports, and particularly when the weather makes visibility difficult, the landing will be under "positive control." Under these circumstances the pilot will call approach control when he is about 30 to 40 miles from landing. From that point on all of his actions will be dictated by the controller in front of his radar screen at or near the airport. The pilot will be told what speed to fly, the altitude, and each change in heading. This is generally known as "being vectored" to the airport or to some point in the sky where an established pattern of flight is to be followed. Such patterns are fully

Navy WAVE Air Controller at a radar screen vectoring military traffic into Miramar Naval Air Station.

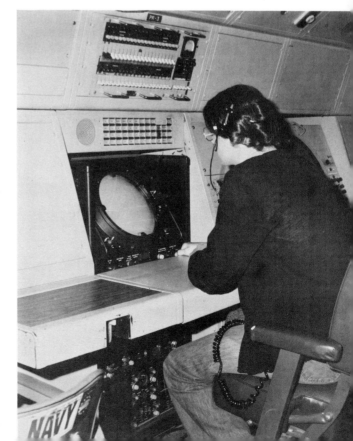

At a "controlled airport" the specialist handling approach control will "hand off" your pilot to the airport tower personnel when you are on your final approach path. "Tower" will then clear you to land.

described in the chapter on the Approach Plates. During a vectored approach the flying companion should have her pencil handy, as instructions come thick and fast. At times static or transmissions from other aircraft make reception poor, and two sets of ears are helpful.

The "friend" manning the Unicom will get his wind speed and direction information from this simple instrument seen at every airport.

At an uncontrolled airport the flying companion has even heavier responsibilities in assisting the pilot. There are great procedural differences for the pilot at uncontrolled airports. These begin many miles from landing. There may be no radio aids, and the maximum help the pilot can anticipate comes from an "airport advisory" he may obtain when he contacts someone on the ground manning the Unicom radio. If the symbol U-1, signifying the presence of a Unicom, is noted next to the airport on the Sectional Chart, the pilot will tune 122.8 mHz and call for an advisory. If there is an answer to this call it usually emanates from the office of a helpful and interested Fixed Base Operator on the field. He provides this service as a courtesy and it is often secondary in importance to other duties in his office. It is seldom a 24 hour service, so the net effect is to make dependence on Unicom a little chancy. Since an uncontrolled airport has no tower or ground control it is the sole responsibility of the pilot to choose the time of landing, the runway, and the parking. Here the flying companion must help in a multitude of ways. She should have firmly fixed in her

Recipe for a Landing

mind—as well as in her notes—the location of the airport, its elevation, and the orientation of the runways. As soon as it is spotted, the windsock or wind tee should be observed and a comment as to the wind direction and speed needs to be made. As the pilot enters the landing pattern, the skies, the taxiways, and the runways should be constantly monitored for other airplanes. It is sad to say that pilots may not be as watchful as they should, and that light aircraft have "blind spots" where the wing or part of the cabin may obstruct a clear view. At an uncontrolled airport vigilance must be doubled as there is no controller to help with traffic.

At this point it is well to describe the "traffic pattern" flown by the pilot prior to landing. Convention has prescribed that a pathway be followed to increase safety and to allow a careful scrutiny of the airport for hazards. Unless otherwise

designated in airport directories or by Notices to Airmen, the pilot will fly the pattern shown. His entry will be at 45 degrees, his turns will be 90 degrees and to the left.

At present the pilot will fly 800 feet above the airport elevation as he enters the landing pattern, although this may later change to 1000 feet, which will make the arithmetic even easier.

It may seem juvenile to point out, but a successful traffic pattern depends on the selection of the proper runway. If the proper procedure is not followed the pilot will find himself crossing the pattern of another runway, with a chance of collision. The flying companion will have available in her notes the orientation of the various runways. By having an airport diagram such as appears on Approach Plates, or in the various airport directories she can help the pilot pick out the correct runway. When dancing in and out

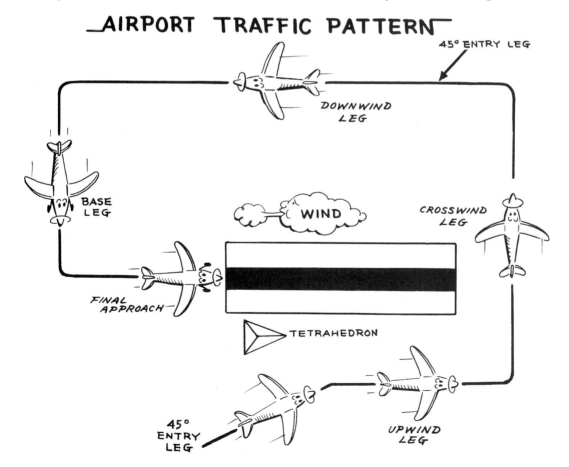

AIRPORT TRAFFIC PATTERN

45° ENTRY LEG

DOWNWIND LEG

BASE LEG

WIND

CROSSWIND LEG

FINAL APPROACH

TETRAHEDRON

45° ENTRY LEG

UPWIND LEG

From White Knuckles to Cockpit Cool

of clouds, during darkness, and at large airports with many runways this identification can be remarkably difficult. Watching other airplanes in a landing pattern may be a great help. The majority of airports have their runways identified by large numbers at each end. Remember that it is necessary to add one zero to the runway number whether seen from the air or read from a directory. For example, if the number 34 appears in the runway information this signifies a 340 degree heading. The arithmetic of runways is further complicated by the need to add two zeros to the runway length as presented in the Sectional Chart; hence, 47 means that the runway is 4700 feet in length.

A comforting and inexpensive item for your flight bag is the PDQ Visual Airport Guide. This device has a yellow side for the traditional left hand landing pattern, and a blue side for right hand patterns. When properly dialed, it gives a picture of the heading and location of your plane in relation to the airport; it also provides a diagram of the landing pattern and the headings your pilot must fly to properly execute the pattern.

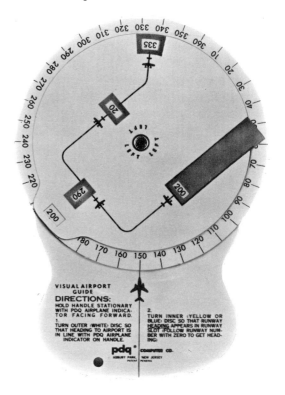

For those who have trouble adding or subtracting 180, and are "thrown" by the 45 degree entry into the pattern, such handy devices as the PDQ computer do all of the work.

GUMP   TWERP

GUMP AND TWERP

These terms are not meant to describe the pilot and his favorite passenger! They are convenient acronyms to summarize important actions by the pilot and his flying cohort as landing is approached.

GUMP stands for:
    Gasoline
    Undercarriage
    Mixture
    Propellers

You may hear your pilot muttering this under his breath as he turns from base leg to final approach. It is a quick reminder that the tanks should be switched to those with adequate fuel should a "go around" be necessary; that the wheels should be down and locked; that the mixture should be rich, and the propellers in the forward position to supply added power in an emergency.

The flying companion complements the actions of the pilot by her contribution to the safety of the landing. Her convenient acronym is also inelegant, but important as a reminder.

TWERP stands for:
    Traffic
    Windsock
    Elevation of the airport
    Radios
    Pumps

Some individual explanation is necessary. Most aircraft collisions take place at or in the immediate vicinity of airports. In fact, a flight of nearly a thousand miles may often be completed with the only other aircraft seen as one approaches the termination of the flight. The pilot has heavy cockpit priorities at the time of landing and his attention may be directed only briefly to the skies around him. The extra pair of eyes provided by the passenger in the right seat can be of inestimable value. This is particularly true at an "uncontrolled" airport; one at which there is no control tower. The pilot usually will be declaring his intentions to land and his position on 122.8, the Unicom frequency; but this may not be monitored by all aircraft in the vicinity

and, in a sense, it is "every man for himself!" If another airplane is in the immediate area; if the course flown by another aircraft seems potentially dangerous; or if a plane appears to be preparing to taxi onto the "active" runway, it is information the pilot needs to know—immediately!!!

The windsock is time-honored, ubiquitous, and quite definite in the wind directional information it presents. The problem is that the darned thing is often hard to spot! Once located, it should be pointed out to the pilot and a comment made to the effect that "the wind is right down the runway," or "the wind is from the left about 20 to 30 degrees." Remember that an airplane lands, whenever possible, "into the wind" to shorten the runway roll. It is a tragic mistake on short runways to land "with the wind," so windsock information is important!

At some remote fields, and particularly in Mexico, the windsock may have disappeared. In that circumstance, you and the

Windsocks come in all sizes and colors, and are very often hard to spot on the field. Be sure to look at the roofs of hangars and other small buildings as well as near the runway. You take off and land "against the wind" to shorten the distance before you have effective lift when taking off, and to shorten the landing roll when you touch down on the runway.

GUMP and TWERP

When neither a windsock nor windtee are available at remote airports, the pilot should be aware of such things as blowing smoke or dust to give him evidence of wind direction prior to landing.

pilot should be watching for wind direction as indicated by blowing smoke, dust from farm machinery, or the direction clothes are blown on a clothesline. These will be rough indicators, but with a short runway such information is important. Occasionally the airport will have wind direction signified by a "windtee." This is a T-like device roughly shaped like a miniature airplane. The proper orientation for landing will be in the direction the "little airplane" is pointing. One note of caution. When the wind tee is visible it is well to look around for a windsock also. For reasons that are diverse a wind tee may be tied into one position or otherwise not swinging freely into the wind. It is reassuring to see a windsock confirming the wind tee information.

Elevation of the airport is information you will already have imparted to your pilot. At the last moment as he is on final, he may again quickly request this figure. It should be available.

Radio settings at the terminal airport have also been checked several miles out, but your pilot may want to confirm the tower frequency or be told ground frequency at the last minute. As you improve your skills, he may ask you to make the necessary changes when frequency switching is commanded by approach control or the tower.

Fuel pumps in most general aviation aircraft are of two types: mechanical fuel pumps driven by the engines, and supplementary electrically operated pumps as "back-ups" should the mechanical pumps fail. Be aware of the manufacturer's recommendations for your plane regarding the position of the pumps during take-offs and landings. The electrical pumps are usually activated by a toggle or rocker switch on the panel and during the landing procedure a gentle reminder to the pilot to flick these switches will confirm your increasing knowledge of airmanship.

STOP

COME AHEAD

CUT ENGINES

ALL CLEAR (O.K.)

EMERGENCY STOP

Signals used by line boys to indicate desired action in moving and parking planes.

SUPERVISING THE LINE BOY

More times than you will care to remember you will be stranded on a hot parking apron to supervise the line boy, while the pilot conveniently disappears into an air conditioned waiting room to "check the weather" or do one of the seemingly endless tasks required in flight planning. These needs seem always to be met in comfortable surroundings. However, "not to worry," as a British friend assures me. At least you are comforted by the knowledge that the airplane has been properly fed and cared for.

As the eager-faced youth greets you with a questioning look, you must remember to remain firm and personally supervise all details. Every Fixed Base Operator would like nothing better than a seasoned mechanic on his flight line. Usually he must settle for boys and girls who love planes and who come and go with the rapidity of jets. So, as the gas-oline truck rolls up, survey it with a practiced eye and be sure that your instructions are followed. Of tremendous importance is the choice of the correct grade of fuel as an improper selection could result in major damage to the engine. This is usually an easy decision as the manufacturer's recommendations regarding the minimum grade of fuel as well as the capacity of each tank are shown by a placard on or adjacent to the filler caps. In the majority of instances the aircraft will use either 80/87 gasoline, which is red in color; 100/130 octane fuel, which is green; or the new low lead fuel tinted blue.

Any deviation suggested by the line boy should be rejected until the decision has been brought to the attention of the pilot with whom the ultimate choice rests. The fuel truck will be plainly labeled, or if fuel is being delivered from a fuel pump, this

FUEL
USE 100/130 GRADE FUEL OR HIGHER ONLY
CAPACITY 40 US GALLONS (37 USABLE)
WITH WINGS LEVEL
CAP. TO TAB BOTTOM 30 GAL. (27 USABLE)
CAP. TO TAB SLOT 35 GAL. (32 USABLE)

CAUTION
DO NOT INSERT FUEL NOZZLE
MORE THAN 3" INTO TANK

This Beechcraft fuel tank is placarded in no uncertain terms. All of the pertinent information is clearly stated, but in spite of this, the helpful co-pilot must operate on the assumption that the line boy may only read Sanskrit and be there to be sure the instructions are followed.

will also be appropriately marked so that you can triple check the correctness of the fuel being delivered to your tanks.

Learn how the caps are properly seated and check them after the line boy has completed the replenishment of fuel. Leave nothing to chance! It is also a good idea to visually check the tanks after they are filled at an intermediate stop before the caps are replaced. This is somewhat difficult on a high wing aircraft but it is much better to "shinny" up a small ladder to personally check the fuel and fuel cap rather than have your flight shortened unnecessarily by the siphoning effect which may occur when a fuel cap has been improperly seated.

When flying in Mexico or when gasoline is being delivered from a large drum, use a chamois as a filter as the gasoline may have both water and sediment. On any flight, but especially into Mexico, a chamois should be part of the equipment carried.

It may seem terribly elementary but you should also be absolutely sure that the line boy is not smoking as he delivers gasoline to your expensive airplane. It is important when a fuel truck is being used that the truck is grounded to the airplane by a wire from the truck hooked to one of the metallic surfaces on the plane. This will prevent an unscheduled Fourth of July celebration induced by a spark of static electricity in an area high in gasoline fumes.

There must never be a question as to the octane rating of the fuel. Fuel trucks are nearly always plainly marked, as are fuel pumps. For safety and for engine life, it is necessary to be sure that the proper fuel is used. This should not be left to the line boy.

An "over the shoulder" technique, particularly in a high wing airplane, controls the hose nozzle and prevents scratching that beautiful paint job.

From White Knuckles to Cockpit Cool

Represented is the ideal. The truck is grounded to the nose wheel to prevent static electricity igniting the gasoline fumes. The fueling is visually checked during the procedure, and the tanks inspected prior to takeoff. At this time the caps should be seen to be properly seated, and the sumps drained to ensure that no water or sediment has been introduced during fueling. When the tanks are filled from drums such as in remote areas, the gasoline should be filtered through a chamois.

By the time the fuel has been delivered, the oil dipstick will have cooled enough to prevent burned fingers and the level of oil can be checked. Oil has a lubricating function, a sealing function, is an effective cleanser, and acts as a cooling agent. For these four reasons the proper level of oil is of vital importance. You know from your experience with automobiles, there are many grades and weights of engine oil. These will be known to your pilot and you should carefully check his recommendation with respect to the weight of oil as well as the oil level. In addition, aircraft engine oil comes in both detergent and nondetergent types. It is absolutely imperative that you be completely sure which of these types is used in the plane in which you are a passenger. Serious engine damage can occur when the wrong type of oil is used. These important points should be entered in your "Line Boy Check List" in the Appendix. At the conclusion of the oil check be sure that the oil filler cap and oil dipstick are securely in position.

When the reckoning time comes with the fixed base operator for the purchase of fuel and oil, the vast majority will accept gasoline credit cards. Since many fixed base operators accept only one or two oil companies' credit cards, it is wise to have several available when a long flight is planned. This will avoid the necessity of dipping into your cash supply when you may be in a city where it is difficult to cash a check. You should save your original credit slip for tax purposes in the event the flight is a business expense and you should inquire of the fixed base operator whether or not it is possible to apply for a tax refund. Many states offer such refunds.

THE
OVERNIGHT STOP

Have a written checklist for an overnight stop! The care of each airplane is so variable that only suggestions are possible. Using the Aztec as our example, we begin by removing any baggage that is necessary for the overnight stop. It is an excellent idea to have packed a small bag containing the minimum clothing and cosmetics for such stops. Close the side curtains and check the instrument panel; double checking to be sure that the Master switch is in the "off" position. If not, a dead battery will greet you in the morning with long delays and much frustration on the part of everyone.

There should be some method of covering the instruments to shade them from the sun as well as from the eyes of radio and instrument "collectors." In our plane the seat belt may be used to anchor the yoke and limit the movement of the ailerons and elevator in the event of high winds during the night. The small pilot's window should be secured. A blanket is a welcome protection for the upholstery at a stop and later can do double duty during flight to protect chilly feet or as a pillow during a short nap by the flying companion. Check the plane door and all baggage compartments to be sure they are securely locked. The brakes should not be left in a set position, however the wheels should be chocked prior to releasing the brakes. This technique will pre-

From White Knuckles to Cockpit Cool

vent rolling when the parking area is on a slight incline, and will hold the plane in position should a wind rise prior to the final tie-down.

Tie-down ropes and chocks are available at the majority of Fixed Base Operator parking areas but for flights into remote areas, ropes should be carried in the aircraft so that the plane is always secure. It is not wise to leave a plane until you have seen it carefully bedded down for the night with the Master switch off, appropriate doors and compartments locked, and the plane thoroughly tied and chocked.

Many motels are very accommodating to the private pilot and will gladly send a car to the airport for the pilot and his passenger. The service is nearly always free but it is usual to tip the boy who does the driving and helps with the bags just as you would a hotel bellman. It is a great pleasure to do this in the majority of instances because unlike many jaded hotel bellhops these people seem to enjoy this part of their job. Often they will evince an interest in looking into the plane and having a brief description of the instruments. Except at large airports it is usually possible for the limousine to be driven directly to the plane so that baggage transfer is a simple job.

Most Fixed Base Operators and many aircraft supply houses make available manuals which give information about motels and resorts that furnish services to the private pilot. As noted elsewhere, these are inexpensive and very convenient during the flight planning phase of the trip.

14

THE NUMBERS GAME

All competent pilots have committed to memory or have readily available in their flight bag the important numbers used in ordinary flight. These are derived from a variety of sources and some are of particular importance, and others of interest to the "on the ball" passenger. As indicated elsewhere in this volume it is very important for the apt flying companion to have ears and pencil at the ready. Radio settings given by transmission to the pilot as well as other data should be jotted down for instant recall. This is particularly vital during instrument flight as radio frequency changes occur rapidly and the pilot has a heavy responsibility merely complying with the multitude of instructions being transmitted to him by the controller. Other numbers have varying degrees of importance but the more you can remember, the more useful you become.

EMERGENCY NUMBERS:

121.5—This is an emergency radio fre-quency and is monitored constantly by a host of ground facilities. It is a "court of last resort" if no other radio facility can be immediately contacted at a time of danger. When supplemented by the distress call "Mayday, Mayday" it is the ultimate signal to ground facilities that a serious problem has occurred. Once contact with the ground has been established such information as to the nature of the emergency, the location and altitude of the aircraft and the immediate plans can be transmitted.

7700—This is a transponder code and signifies an emergency. When tuned, this code gives the ground facility location information and coupled with voice contact with the ground offers the best chance of effective assistance.

7600—This is also a transponder code and indicates radio failure in your aircraft. This will allow air traffic specialists to clear the skies in your vicinity and let your pilot land and effect correction of the problem.

Ever vigilant air controllers in all civilian and military facilities monitor the emergency frequencies. A call to 121.5 will be answered by any station within reach of the aircraft radio, and the transponder codes 7700 and 7600 also result in an immediate response. Here a Navy controller is at his console during a late night shift—ready to help any civilian or military pilot in distress.

HELPFUL NUMBERS:

122.2 or 122.3—These are "simplex" frequencies for radio transmission and allow two-way conversation with Flight Service Stations. A whole group of other simplex frequencies from 122.25 to 122.45, and from 122.55 to 122.75 are being phased in, and should there by no response from 122.2 or 122.3 these can be tried.

122.8—This is a Unicom number for contact with uncontrolled airports without towers. It is a radio frequency that is widely used and there is often a great deal of "chatter" from various small airports and pilots in the vicinity. This frequency is used to get airport advisory information concerning the traffic, altimeter, and wind conditions at your terminal airport. Courteous people on the ground will often make motel reservations, call transportation, or suggest repair facilities if requested. It is important to be certain when using this frequency that you are conversing with the correct airport. You are often within range of several Unicoms and confusion can occur.

122.0—This is a "Flight Watch" frequency with the most current weather and en route conditions gained from pilot reports and access to National weather information. Not all of the United States is covered by this extremely useful service and the initial favorable response by pilots will probably make it nation-wide in the near future.

Approach Control Frequencies—These are noted on approach plates or can be obtained by voice contact with Flight Service Stations. These frequencies are used to call for traffic information and to establish radar contact while still 20 to 40 miles from large airports.

ATIS (Automatic Terminal Information Service)—This is a radio frequency containing current information as to sky conditions, altimeter setting, wind speed and direction, and any indicated radio frequencies to contact as the pilot approaches the airport. The correct ATIS frequency can be obtained from approach plates; the **Airman's Information Manual, Part III;** The Sectional Chart, as well as a number of commercially produced manuals.

Altimeter Setting—This is an ever-changing number and needs periodic up-

68

dating. It will be mentioned during the recording of the ATIS and at initial contact with a control tower, Flight Service Station, or Approach Control.

Tower and Ground Frequencies—These radio frequencies will be available from a number of sources but are always noted on approach plates and can always be obtained by voice contact with a Flight Service Station.

Runway Orientation—Airport diagrams will give the headings and lengths of each runway. These are visually reproduced on approach plates but are also contained in many manuals which can be purchased inexpensively or come as a bonus when one joins various pilot's organizations. On the Sectional chart and on IFR charts the description will list only the length of the longest runway with the necessity to add two zeros; hence 50 would indicate that the longest runway is 5,000 feet. On all navigation aids, the runway number necessitates the addition of one zero; hence RWY 25, means a heading of 250 degrees, and RWY 6 indicates a heading of 60 degrees.

Airport Elevation—This figure is necessary to the pilot in setting up his final approach and landing. It is present in many places, but always on an approach plate, a Sectional chart, an IFR chart, the **Airman's Information Manual** and many good commercial manuals. On both the Sectional and IFR Charts it is the first number in sequence in the descriptive material listed by each airport.

NUMBERS
"BEYOND THE CALL OF DUTY":
Runway Reciprocal—This is the "down wind heading" in the landing pattern and is derived from adding 18 to the landing runway heading if that number is less than 18; or subtracting 18 if it exceeds 18. Examples would be: landing RWY 17; downwind heading would be 35, or 350 degrees—landing runway 28; downwind heading would be 10, or 100 degrees.

Pattern Altitude—This figure currently is 800 feet plus the airport elevation and signifies the correct altitude to fly as one enters the landing pattern. It is anticipated that this figure will be changed to 1,000 feet plus the airport elevation in the near future and this will simplify the arithmetic.

123.0—This is the Unicom frequency at airports with control towers. This is usually manned by a fixed base operator on the field. He will normally be quite accommodating with respect to making arrangements for fuel, lodging, or calling friends to meet you.

1200—This is a transponder code for VFR flight.

122.1—This is a radio frequency that will reach Flight Service Stations, often through remoted sites. Return information will be heard on the VOR, so this must be tuned correctly to complete two-way communication. When the usual simplex frequencies are very busy this is often an excellent alternative.

Density Altitude—Although "beyond the call of duty" this calculation taken from charts printed in the Appendix or calculated from the computer is a vital number; particularly on a hot, humid day and a proposed take-off from a high altitude airport!!!!!

15

THE
AVIATION COMPUTER

The computer is generally considered to be a bastion only the pilot is capable of conquering. Like the instrument panel, first contact with an aviation computer is disconcerting and far more information can be obtained from these "circular slide rules" than you will ever need in thousands of hours of flying. But also like the instrument panel, once the initial shock has worn off you will quickly find that with minimal familiarity you can solve a number of problems and both inform yourself as to the progress of your flight as well as be of help to the pilot when his attentions are fully taken by other cockpit problems.

Nearly all commercially available and popular computers supply the same data. In this discussion the Jeppesen CSG-2A Computer is used; however, with minor adaptations any model will offer nearly the same versatility. Content yourself with things that are both important and easy to solve! Forget the "wind face" of the instrument and leave wind triangle problems to your pilot. These do not have practical significance except in rare circumstances. Modern navigation aids and the auto-pilot have made such problems esoteric.

With that off of your mind, do become familiar with the simple problems of **conversions.** In the kitchen, butter and oleomargarine may both look alike but their performance in baking may be different. Much the same is true when we regard miles or temperature. In a problem involving distance if the unit is miles (and in the United States it will be), miles must all be converted to either statute miles or nautical miles. Anything else would be comparing apples and oranges. Hence, a calculation taken from a flight plan filed by your pilot where an IFR chart has been used will undoubtedly be expressed in nautical miles as that is the unit utilized in IFR charts. If you make a measurement on your Sectional Chart using the plotter and obtain a value in statute miles, you have a problem in conversion. Here the computer will help. On the face of the more popular models will be two arrows connected by a bar—one arrow labeled "naut" and the other "stat." Merely place the "stat" arrow on the number of statute miles taken from your plotter measurement and read the value under "naut." This will be the equivalent in nautical miles and you will now have all oranges to work with as you advance in solving problems. Example: on the Los Angeles Sectional Chart measuring with the plotter from Capistrano to Gillespie Field will show 61 statute miles. Conversion to nautical miles results in a value of 53 nautical.

As with miles, so it is with miles-per-hour (MPH). This value also must be converted so that all numbers reflect either statute MPH or nautical MPH (Knots). If you are working a time and distance problem and your distance has been measured with your plotter in statute miles, the reading in MPH taken from your DME (Distance Measuring Equipment) will be in nautical MPH and must be converted for the problem to be accurately solved. Example: speed read from the DME is 140 nautical miles per hour. The time to fly from Capistrano to Gillespie necessitates conversion of the 61 statute miles to 53 nautical miles, or the 140 nautical MPH to 161 statute MPH to arrive at the solution.

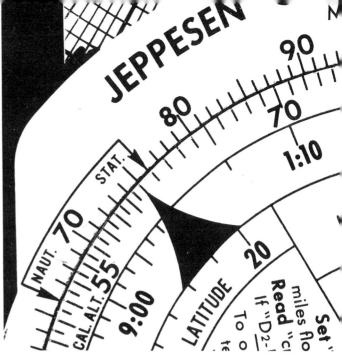

Just as in sewing, match the notches! Place the "stat" arrow on the number of statute miles and read the value under the "naut" arrow. The conversion can also be made from "naut" to "stat."

Conversion of temperature from Fahrenheit (F) to Celsius (C) may also be necessary. In solving the very important problem of density altitude, the temperature scale on the computer is noted in Celsius (C). If you know only the temperature in Fahrenheit you can either work a "hard to remember" equation or simply match up the numbers on the temperature conversion scale. **Example:** Outside air temperature taken from the thermometer shows 50 degrees Fahrenheit. Conversion shows this to be 10 degrees Celsius.

In this problem of conversion, one quickly sees that 140 nautical miles equal 161 statute miles—and so it is with "miles per hour."

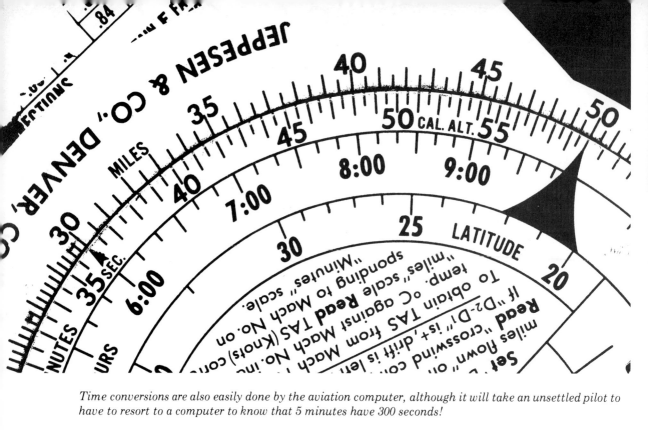

Time conversions are also easily done by the aviation computer, although it will take an unsettled pilot to have to resort to a computer to know that 5 minutes have 300 seconds!

Conversion of time from seconds, to minutes, to hours is so common in ordinary life that the computer is seldom necessary, but the "minutes" scale is also conveniently calculated in hours. Similarly you can either make a mental substitution using the same scale, substituting seconds for minutes and minutes for hours, since the factor is the same, i.e. 60; or you can really be lazy and find the small arrow on the computer labeled "sec." Place the large arrow (60) at the number of minutes, using the miles scale and read the number of seconds at the small "sec" arrow. **Example**: To find the number of seconds in 5 minutes, place the large arrow on 50, and read the answer at the small arrow—30. Since you have an extra zero at the 5 (50), you add a zero to the answer, and 30 becomes 300—the correct answer.

Once conversions have been correctly made you are ready to calculate some important problems that are both practical and simple.

The first is the solution of **Density Altitude** problems. Tables for these values are available (see appendix) but this information can be neatly and simply displayed on your computer. The density

of the atmosphere is of extreme importance in view of its effect on lift and drag. Air is a gas and the density of any gas is changed by changing temperature and pressure. Density altitude reflects a calculation of theoretical density of a standardized atmosphere at a given altitude. As tough as that sentence is to conceptualize, it is that value that reflects aircraft performance rather than the indicated altitude read off of your altimeter. When you hear your pilot friends remarking about the potential dangers of a takeoff when it is "high, hot, and humid" they are really inferring that the density altitude is high and the airplane will not perfrom as well as when the day is cool, dry, and the takeoff near sea level.

Only two numbers are needed to arrive at a solution of density altitude: 1. temperature in Celsius. 2. pressure altitude, simply read off of your aircraft's altimeter when set at 29.92 inches of mercury.

Your observation of the outside air temperature reading and, if necessary, a conversion to Celsius gives the first number. Your pilot can be asked to change the altimeter temporarily to

The Temperature Conversion Scale is a fixed scale drawn on the outer ring of the Jeppesen CSG-9 Computer pictured above. Turn the picture upside down and you will see a portion of the scale for changing minutes into hours. The number 70 represents minutes. Under the 70 are the numbers 1:10. This means there is 1 hour and 10 minutes in 70 minutes. 80 minutes equals 1 hour and 20 minutes and 85 minutes 1 hour and 25 minutes. This method is used to read this entire ring of the computer. (The Temperature Conversion Scale is located on the "wind side" of the CSG-2A.)

29.92, or you can do this yourself. Read the resultant pressure altitude; jot it down and then reset the altimeter to its proper position. Now match the two numbers in the density altitude section on the face of the computer and read the number in the density altitude window. The resultant value is often a shocking surprise on a hot day. Your pilot should be informed of the density altitude and either you or he can obtain the necessary runway length from aircraft performance figures in your own aircraft handbook.

Near San Diego there is a lovely recreational area at Big Bear Lake, with a small airport nearby. This is a very popular spot in both summer and winter. The altitude is 6750 feet and the runway length 5800 feet. An unsuspecting pilot who flies in and out of this airport with impunity during the skiing season could make a fatal error in the same aircraft in midsummer when the temperature may reach 95 degrees Fahrenheit (35 degrees Celsius) and the density altitude approximates 10,450 feet. Under these circum-

stances the rate of climb will drop to nearly 58% of normal and the increase in takeoff run will rise 110%!!!!!!! Los Alamos airport in New Mexico is another good example of a location with both summer and winter recreational areas. The altitude is 7173 feet and in summer at 95 degrees Fahrenheit, the density altitude exceeds 10,800 feet. With a runway length of only 4800 feet, the capability of some fully loaded aircraft to become airborne is exceeded. The airplane "thinks" it is at 10,800 feet and climbs like a housewife back from shopping and a four-hour P.T.A. meeting!

Time, Speed, and **Distance** problems are next. So long as you have your conversions made and it is all oranges—not oranges and apples—you can solve any of the three values if you have the other two available. In the CSG-2A model this is disarmingly simple, and you really could use the computer in the kitchen to compute a problem in cooking a roast where the three values would be weight, oven temperature, and time. A housewife does it every day—or did when meat was cheaper—and with simple arithmetic; the same way the computer solves the problem in flying.

Look at the face of the computer. **Distance** in miles is the outside ring. **Time** in minutes and hours appears on the inner ring. The **Speed** is represented by the large arrow. A moment of careful viewing of the arithmetic face of any computer will demonstrate these scales are nicely labeled and easy to find.

To find **Speed** rotate the inner dial until the time it took you to cover a given distance lies directly opposed to the miles you have travelled. Look at the arrow. It points to your speed over the ground. Voila! The answer! **Example:** Time is 27 minutes to cover 61 statute miles. Answer: 136 statute miles-per-hour.

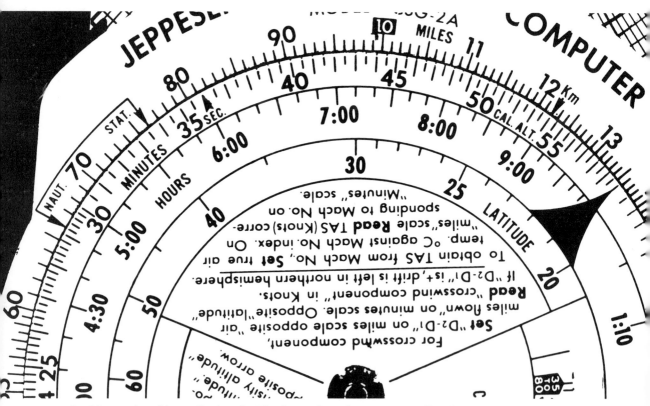

In this speed problem, aligning the 27 minutes it took to cover 61 miles shows the arrow pointing to 136 miles per hour.

The Aviation Computer

To find **Time** of arrival, merely put the arrow on your speed; look along the outer circle to the miles yet to be travelled. Look directly under that number to the inner dial and you read the time in minutes to your destination. **Example:** Speed is 140 nautical miles-per-hour and there are 70 nautical miles remaining to fly. Answer: 30 minutes to the airport.

To check **Distance,** set the arrow on your speed; look along the inner dial to find the time in minutes you have flown. Exactly at that point on the outer circle will be the miles you have covered. Simple subtraction from the point-to-point total quickly gives the remaining miles to be traversed. Simple, isn't it? **Example:** Speed is 140 nautical miles-per-hour, flown in 45 minutes. Distance is 105 nautical miles. In a trip of 200 nautical miles, there are 95 miles remaining.

Before closing this chapter the obvious must be stressed. At speeds reached by the modern light aircraft any of these values must be continuously updated. Altitude changes, variation in power or propeller settings, alteration of wind speed and direction, as well as other factors make constant review of results profitable and interesting.

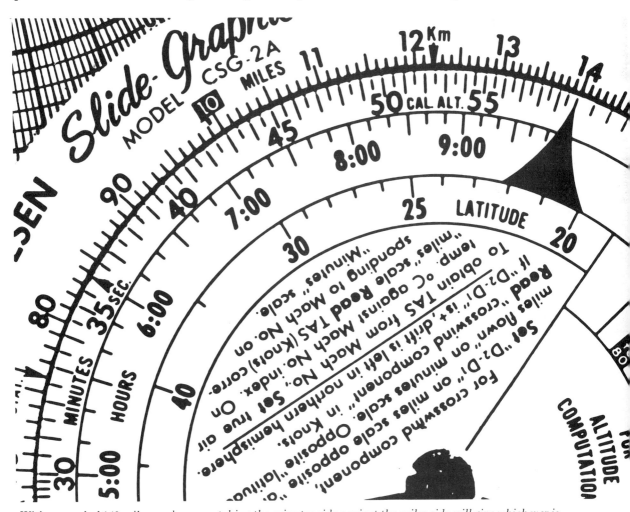

With a speed of 140 miles per hour, matching the minutes side against the miles side will give whichever is the unknown.

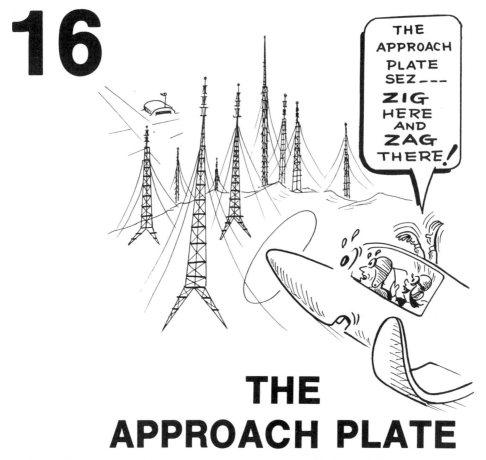

The approach plate sez --- ZIG here and ZAG there!

16

THE APPROACH PLATE

Several years ago there was a popular book entitled **The Battle is the Payoff.** In a successful flight "the landing is the payoff" since the objective of the flight is achieved. Then, for most flying companions on a vacation flight, the real fun begins. To aid the pilot in his preparation for landing at an unfamiliar airport, the Approach Plate contains a wealth of information.

These handy little items become important for these reasons:

1. a tremendous amount of crucial information is condensed onto one small sheet.

2. the material may be needed in rapid-fire succession.

3. the pilot is busiest with other cockpit priorities when Approach Plate information is needed.

In a sense the Approach Plate is the "city map" compared with the "regional map" we use in driving an automobile. It details in very exacting fashion the course the pilot must fly if he is in instrument conditions. More than this however, Approach Plates are informative on even the brightest, clearest CAVU (**C**lear **A**nd **V**isibility **U**nlimited) day. Reproduced are typical Approach Plates, produced by the National Ocean Survey and the Jeppesen Company. You will undoubtedly be working from either a Government chart or a "Jepp." Prior to the flight it is wise to locate the appropriate plates so that they will be available when needed. Their vintage should also be checked as TV towers and high-rise condominiums seem to sprout overnight and current charts are mandatory.

Now for the important information that will allow you to follow your pilot's superlative performance in a relaxed manner.

1. **ATIS (Automatic Terminal Information Service):** This is a radio frequency which you should monitor, with your pilots permission, when you are still 20-30 miles from your destination. At many airports a recorded broadcast will

The Approach Plate

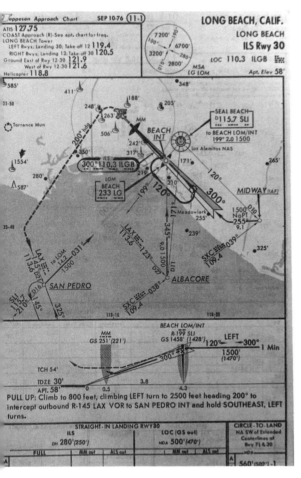

indicate sky conditions, wind direction and speed, current altimeter setting, probable runway, and approach control frequency. These should be jotted down for later reference as all may be important to your pilot as he "sets up" his landing.

2. **Altitude**: This figure should be noted as it will dictate the "pattern altitude" your pilot will fly.

3. **Radio Frequencies:** Any large, busy airport will have one or more approach control frequencies, a tower frequency, and a ground control frequency. If you are ready with these when asked, you will have been a valued aide. In time, your pilot will depend on your setting the radio freqencies in advance of the landing.

4. **VOR, DME, ILS, or NDB Approaches**: These are not derived from scrabble, and a word of explanation is needed. In instrument conditions, the time your pilot is under the most pressure and may need your help, one of several techniques may be assigned by approach control to guide him to a safe landing. The controller may say, "66 Yankee is cleared for a VOR approach to runway 25 Right." This means that a particular route has been chosen, and to fly that route the right map (Approach Plate) will be needed. You will be of assistance if you

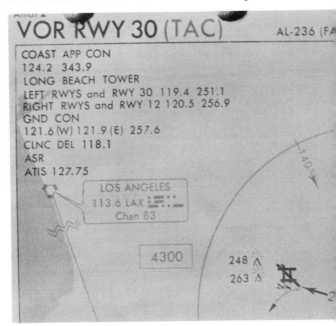

Observe that this is the proper "map" for VOR RWY 30 (TAC). If the controller tells your pilot to use a DME, ILS or NDB Approach you would look for one of those headings on the Approach Plate. Radio Frequencies are listed on these charts.

are ready to supply the "VOR RWY 25R" Approach Plate at the moment the controller has made this selection. In a VOR approach the flying companion usually has little more to do than have the altimeter setting, wind direction and speed, and airport altitude available. The VOR frequency has probably been tuned several miles prior to arriving at the airport control zone.

Similarly, 66 Yankee may be "cleared to ILS 25 Left to report at the outer marker." As with the VOR approach, there will be an Approach Plate entitled "ILS RWY 25L" and this must be supplied. The pilot must "dial in" the correct ILS radio frequency, and a radio change will be needed when this information is received. The ILS (Instrument Landing System) tells you that your pilot is going to be required to fly a very narrow pathway in the sky to a "localizer" which has a specific radio frequency. This is clearly marked on the Approach Plate. Since it is such a vital piece of information it will be a great help to your pilot if you have checked that frequency, making doubly sure that it coincides with the radio change your pilot has made. Transposing 108.9 with 109.8 in dense clouds could be a serious error! It is also good policy to note the compass heading of the localizer as a reminder for your pilot should he require it.

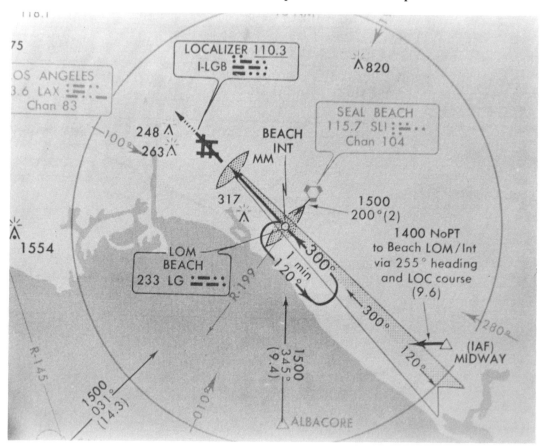

This part of the Approach Plate designates one of the "instrument approaches" to Long Beach Daugherty Field. This uses an ILS (Instrument Landing System) technique to follow a prescribed pathway in the sky to a safe landing. Here the "localizer" has a frequency of 110.3 and setting the aircraft navigation receiver on that frequency will allow the pilot to fly an accurate track, first to the LOM (Outer Marker), then to the MM (Middle Marker), and on into Runway 30. An added feature of this particular approach is the addition of a radio beacon with a frequency of 233, to which the ADF can be tuned, and which will point directly to the Outer Marker.

The Approach Plate

A DME approach is a rare exercise and you should only be aware of the technique of tuning the DME (Distance Measuring Equipment) to the correct frequency.

The NDB approach is also infrequent, although at small, remote airports it may be the only one available. NDB stands for "Non-directional Beacon" and involves the use of the ADF (Automatic Direction Finder). This will be identified on the Approach Plate with a number, i.e. 339, and a Morse Code identification transmitted audibly such as C-D-E (—·—·—···).

When the ADF is correctly tuned to the beacon you will hear the Morse Code repetitively and the ADF needle will point accurately to the beacon. Since some fine tuning is often necessary for an accurate fix, the pilot may want the ADF tuned to the general vicinity of the frequency many miles from the terminal airport; then turned on and fine-tuned a few miles from landing.

5.**Runway Orientation**: On an Approach Plate there is a graphic "picture" of the various runways and taxiways of an airport. When arriving at a metropolitan airfield your pilot may want to glance quickly at the airport diagram. You may be able to help him identify his assigned runway by visual inspection of the airfield from the cockpit, and comparison with the diagram in your hand. Always remember that a runway heading should be visualized as an extension of a "compass rose." The "threshold" or "touchdown point" of runway 9 would be visualized as an extension of a 90 degree heading as seen on a compass rose.

As one uses Approach Plates, more and more information will be evident. Your pilot may reach the point where he will ask you to identify intersections near the airport, the miles from the outer marker to touchdown, his correct altitude as he

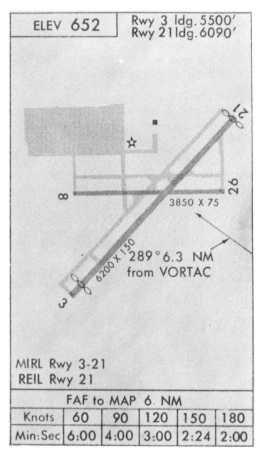

The Approach Plate also contains an airport diagram. This identifies the runway headings and lengths. Taxi-ways are also outlined, and the tower position identified. That mysterious FAF to MAP 6 NM really has an English interpretation: final approach fix to missed approach position is 6 nautical miles. Even the time this will take to fly at various approach speeds is listed in the little boxes below— hence the value of a stop watch, or a watch with a second hand. The flying companion can be the equivalent of a crown jewel if she has the information in the little portion of the approach plate committed to memory or jotted down and ready to produce. The elevation of the airport is also found on this part of the Approach Plate.

crosses a VOR. You can assist as much as you wish, and with increased knowledge a complex landing pattern will be more interesting and increase your respect for the pilot. Two heads are better than one!

17

THE INSTRUMENT PANEL

In modern general aviation aircraft the first view of the instrument panel by the novice will absolutely convince her of the intelligence, wizardry, and brilliance of the pilot. If the pilot is a man he may want to foster this misconception by keeping the secrets of the instruments to himself, thereby extending his feeling of importance. Never mind that he would be totally lost in a modern kitchen confronted with the myriad controls on dishwashers, dryers, washing machines, and self-cleaning ovens. Aircraft instruments can be made to appear particularly mysterious as they relate to flight, which we have mentioned is still regarded with some mysticism.

The panel is complex, but with a small amount of explanation the rudiments will become clear and the flight will be much more interesting if the companion can share the secrets imparted by the gauges and dials in front of her eyes. There is an added facet of improved safety. The pilot conceivably could miss some significant data in his routine scan of the panel that would be noted by the knowledgeable passenger. Anyone who has glanced into the cabin of a modern jetliner knows how many dials, gauges, switches, lights, and levers can be crammed into a small space. Remarkably enough the average well-equipped general aviation airplane contains smaller equivalents of these very same instruments and controls. Certainly such an aircraft will include the majority of those necessary to safely experience the relatively low levels of altitude in which the general aviation aircraft usually operates.

The panel can be conveniently divided into:

   a. Engine instruments
   b. Flight instruments
   c. Navigation aids
   d. Radio
   e. Emergency gear

Each will be described individually and briefly. As interest increases in their function, your pilot can expand (with in-

The Instrument Panel

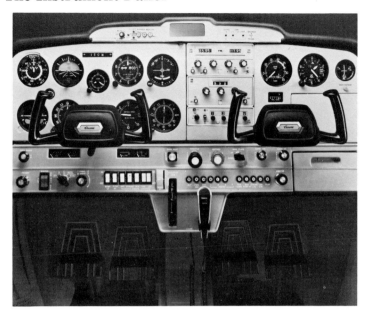

The instrument panel is the "dashboard" of this Cessna aircraft. There is no possible way to convince any flying companion or "first time" pilot that the apparent maze of dials and gauges can be easily understood. In actual fact, the instrument panel will quickly become as familiar as the gasoline gauge, alternator dial, and engine temperature gauge of the standard automobile. After a few flights the "novice" will be peering into other aircraft on the field and quickly identifying all of the instruments with ease.

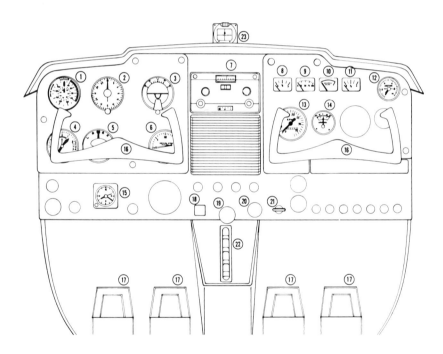

Instrument Panel

1. Airspeed indicator
2. Gyroscopic compass
3. Artificial horizon
4. Altimeter
5. Turn-and-bank indicator
6. Vertical speed (rate-of-climb—descent) indicator
7. VHF navigation — communication radio
8. Fuel gauge (left tank)
9. Oil pressure gauge
10. Oil temperature gauge
11. Fuel gauge (right tank)
12. Suction indicator (run by vacuum pump, which activates gyroscopic instruments)

13. Tachometer (measures revolutions per minute of propeller)
14. Battery — generator indicator
15. Clock
16. Control wheel (dual)
17. Rudder pedals
18. Carburetor heat control
19. Throttle control
20. Fuel-air mixture control
21. Wing flaps control
22. Trim tab control
23. Magnetic compass

creased respect for your perception) and you can supplement your information with more sophisticated knowledge gained from a formal ground school or any one of a number of excellent technical volumes on aviation. This is an admittedly brief overview, but should familiarize you with enough to allow you to be helpful and reasonably informed.

a. Engine instruments:

In the usual panel these are arrayed together and in a twin engine aircraft each will be duplicated. They include:

1. Oil pressure: As would be anticipated from your knowledge of an automobile an internal combustion engine is lubricated by oil. An effective pressure must be maintained or the engine will overheat and, paradoxically, may become so hot that it will "freeze." The oil pressure gauge shows the usual warning colors of red and yellow and the normal operating area colored in green. During the takeoff there may be a momentary surge into the upper area of the yellow warning area or even near the red line, but in the normally operating engine the needle will quickly return to green and remain there throughout flight.

2. Cylinder head temperature: A probe which measures the temperature of one or more cylinders in the engine reflects itself with a gauge included in the engine instruments. Your pilot will be conversant with the normal operating range and this varies contingent on the particular engine and the mixture settings the pilot might select. A consistently rising cylinder head temperature is a source of concern and should be pointed out to the pilot if it occurs. This usually means that the air/gasoline mixture going through the carburetor or fuel injection system is "lean" and merely needs enrichening. It is always important to monitor this gauge.

3. Exhaust gas temperature: Many well-equipped aircraft do not have this feature but like the cylinder head temperature it is another check on the

engine heat and the efficiency of the use of fuel. Your pilot will inform you should you show interest, of the normal ranges that are "in the green." In these days of emphasis on fuel economy and the rising cost of aviation gasoline this accessory gains importance.

4. Fuel gauges: It is sad to relate that fuel gauges in general aviation aircraft are only rather rough indicators of the fuel supply. Much more accurate is experience gained by the pilot in the operation of the airplane, and simple computer checks of his "gallons per hour" as fuel is consumed. Nevertheless on a very long flight or in significant instrument conditions the pilot may have his priorities directed elsewhere and the flying companion should make mention of a fuel gauge that is approaching the "empty" mark. If she is particularly on the ball she will note the time at which tanks were switched so that subsequent calculations can be made if an alternate airport is selected or unexpected headwinds delay the flight.

5. Vacuum: Strictly speaking this is not a pure engine instrument as the vacuum pump is used to drive the gyro-instruments elsewhere displayed on the panel; but it is driven by the engines and usually arrayed with the engine instruments. Failure of the vacuum pump in instrument conditions denies your pilot vital information, and although he can quickly compensate by "partial panel" flying, his job is more complex and if vacuum pump malfunction is not noted immediately there could be a brief period where the false data fed to him by the gyro instruments would have potential danger. There are norms for effective vacuum and although these vary they are usually in the range of 4-5 inches of mercury. The display may also have a warning flag or button that pops out should the pump fail.

6. Manifold pressure: This gauge reflects the power setting chosen by your pilot for climb-out and cruise and is determined by the position of the throt-

The Instrument Panel

tle. The numbers measure inches of manifold pressure and in a normally aspirated engine may characteristically be 25" during maximum climb, 22" at cruise, and 13-15" while negotiating the landing pattern. There is wide variation and this is particularly marked in turbocharged engines. In a sense, this value reflects how "hard" your aircraft engine is working and will have a direct relationship with fuel consumption.

7. Propeller revolutions per minute (RPM): As with manifold pressure settings your pilot will elect varying propeller settings. These will differ dependent on whether one is on climb-out or at cruise, and the factors of fuel economy are also related to this choice. The only time the flying companion becomes aware of propeller settings is in a twin engine airplane when there is an annoying whine of varying pitch when the propellers are "out of synch;" not synchronously set. Minor changes in the speed of one propeller will clear this immediately but its presence does not mean that anything is wrong with propeller function.

8. Fuel flow meter: Another gauge indicates in very rough fashion the rate of fuel flow in gallons per hour. Near sea level and during maximum engine output for takeoff, as well as during landings where sudden acceleration might be needed this gauge will show the maximum. As altitude is gained and the need for a rich gasoline mixture reduces, the mixture is gradually "leaned" by reducing the mixture control on the console. At takeoff from high altitude airports such as Los Alamos or Santa Fe, New Mexico some leaning of the mixture on the ground is necessary for maximum engine output, and should be remembered.

The controls that dictate manifold pressure (the throttle), the propeller RPM and the air/gasoline mixture are often color-coded for quick recognition and safety. The usual coding is a black handle for the throttle, blue for the propeller, and red for the mixture. In at least one major make of aircraft the sequence from left to right for these controls is: throttle, propeller, mixture. This is particularly important in twin engine models where shutting down an engine may be necessary and the six engine and propeller controls must be quickly and accurately identified.

9. Electrical system: As with vacuum pumps, the electrical system is an engine instrument in a round-about sense. The integrity of the system is necessary to start the airplane and a portion of the panel display is taken up with a series of toggle or rocker switches that include the master switch which controls all electrical output from the electrical system, magneto switches necessary to supply spark to ignite the air/fuel mixture and start the engine, the system of lights for night flying and a whole host of breaker switches which may have to be re-set if there has been a temporary over-load. An ammeter display is also present. The flying companion need only know where the master switch is located, as it should be promptly turned off if there is that rarest of all emergencies—smoke in the cabin from incipient fire.

b. Flight instruments:

1. Altimeter: This flight instrument translates barometric pressure into altitude above sea level. During a long flight and particularly during unstable weather conditions the altimeter will have to be re-set at periodic intervals. This information is obtained by a radio call to a nearby airport or Flight Service Station where the data will be supplied. When your pilot calls for airport advisory information, the altimeter setting will always be supplied and the flying companion can be of assistance by jotting it down so that no error is made in setting the instrument. A mistake results in an inaccurate altitude display. In other countries the barometric pressure may be supplied in millibars rather than inches as it is in the United States. A courteous request to the foreign tower will quickly supply the value in inches and allow the appropriate correction. In addition to the standard pressure altimeter seen in all aircraft, some supplement this with a "radar altimeter." This instrument actually measures the height of the craft above terrain by sending and receiving electronic impulses to the ground. This avoids the necessary simple mathematics of the pressure altimeter which reads the height above sea level, but its expense has prevented widespread use in general aviation.

2. Airspeed indicator: When driving in an automobile, speed can be easily related to the circumference of the wheels moving over the highway. Measuring airspeed is a much tougher proposition and the starting point is the force of the wind impacting against the surfaces of the plane in flight. A specific instrument known as the Pitot tube is used. This tube, usually mounted under the wing or on the nose of the aircraft, measures the ram effect of the air striking it. This is translated into airspeed through the "relative wind" which may have only a rough correlation with the speed over the ground. This latter value must be calculated with the use of the computer, or electronically displayed by using the distance measuring equipment if that instrument is available. As an example, an aircraft showing an airspeed on the airspeed indicator of 140 knots, but flying against a 10 knot headwind will actually be travelling over the ground at 130 knots for each hour of flight. As wind speed and direction changes and engine settings are changed, updating the time of arrival and fuel use will be necessary at frequent intervals. In icing conditions the Pitot tube must be heated to avoid partial obstruction with ice and reduction of the ram effect of the outside air. Such obstruction will result in erroneous airspeed values.

3. Needle and ball: This instrument is also known as the "turn and bank indicator" and is seen in every aircraft, no matter how sophisticated. It is really two instruments in one. The ball acts like a surveyor's plumb line and is purely a gravity instrument. If the aircraft is flying "out of trim" the ball will shift to one side or the other, reflecting the pull of gravity or centrifugal force. The needle is a "turn" instrument and will point in the direction of the turn faithfully and reasonably quantitatively. For the beginner these two instruments combined into one are readily understandable and very trustworthy.

4. Artificial horizon: With increased experience the flying companion will be able to judge the "attitude" of the airplane by a quick glance at the artificial horizon. This circular display shows a line reflecting the horizon and a small dot or minute figure of an airplane representing the position of the nose of the aircraft with respect to the horizon. The problem with the novice is that things seem reversed with respect to the true horizon and it takes a few hours of careful inspection of this instrument with reference to the ground before it "makes sense." Until it does, a scan of the needle and ball will set things straight. In instrument conditions the artificial horizon becomes of major importance and you will see your pilot almost huddled in front of this instrument and the gyro compass so that he may maintain proper heading and attitude of the aircraft. It is under these conditions that an intelligent, knowledgeable scan of the other flight and engine instruments by the flying companion can be reassuring to the pilot.

5. Rate of climb: A circular dial will indicate the rate of climb or descent. This instrument has an inherent lag as your pilot will show you, and it must settle down for a few moments before it is an accurate representation of altitude change. The instrument is a particular use in timed descents in instrument conditions and your pilot will refer to it under these circumstances. This is also true in timed climb-outs when a given navigational fix is to be reached in a specified period of time.

6. Auto-pilots: These are expensive and handy conveniences that vary in their sophistication. The simplest is a "wing leveller" that will merely hold the aircraft level and hold a pre-set heading. Some are so complex that, when properly coupled with a flight director, can nearly execute a "hands off" landing with multiple headings, rates of descent, and near hairline locking to a glide slope. A flying companion in an aircraft with an auto-pilot probably should know the technique of turning the wing leveller mode on, and the technique of disengaging the auto-pilot should a serious emergency occur to the pilot. Engaging the wing leveller would allow time to be of help and to "think through" an emergency while the aircraft kept a level, accurate heading. Disengaging the auto-pilot would be necessary before any attempt at landing.

7. Trim adjustments: These may be mechanical and activated by a crank on the roof of the cockpit or elsewhere on the panel by a rotating wheel or handle. In addition to this they may be electrically controlled and activated by a button or knob. The objective is to make the aircraft track through the sky in a straight and level condition without slipping or sliding. The needle and ball instrument is used to monitor this, and minor changes in the rudder will allow the ball to settle into its most dependent position. Small changes in the horizontal tail surface will allow the controls to be easily held in a correct position. A properly trimmed aircraft will continue in a nearly "hands off" course.

8. Outside air temperature: This is simply a thermometer mounted outside the aircraft with the outside temperature recorded visually in the cabin. This has two values: in calculating the true air-speed and density altitude, and in warning when freezing conditions are imminent. In cloudy weather or during flights in rain or mist it is helpful for the flying companion to occasionally note the temperature as when it approaches 32 degrees Fahrenheit, or 0 degrees Celsius freezing conditions can be expected and remedial action on the part of the pilot is necessary.

c. Navigation aids:

1. Wet compass: From almost time immemorial navigators have depended on the magnetic compass. On slow moving platforms it functions well and so long as its inherent error caused by the difference between magnetic North and true North is realized, it is nearly infallible. On a rapidly moving platform such as an aircraft, with sudden changes of both altitude and direction, all sorts of errors occur which take many moments to correct. For this reason the gyro compass which is more stable is used in aircraft. The wet compass, however, remains the frame of reference and all settings of the gyro compass are initially taken from the wet compass. The flying companion will note immediately some of the "errors" the wet compass makes because of inertia. Rapid turns to the right will initially be shown as a left turn. With dives or climbs on a direct heading the compass will indicate a turn. The only thing the flying companion might periodically check is the fluid level in the wet compass. There are seals that may leak after a period of years and particularly in climates featured by rapid changes in temperature and humidity. Since the gyro compass derives its headings from the wet compass a drop in fluid level with a resultant change in accuracy could create a major error. It should also be recalled that the wet compass does react to magnetism and any metallic object placed in proximity to the wet compass should be checked by moving it near the compass to see if there is a deflection. If so, the object should be stowed several feet from the panel to avoid any influence by a false magnetic signal. Such things as flashlights, knives, and screw drivers which might be kept in a glove compartment may be offenders.

2. Gyro compass: As noted above, this instrument was developed to stabilize compass headings and is a gyro instrument dependent on an accurate initial setting using the wet compass as a reference, and adequate vacuum to effectively spin the gyro at appropriate speeds. There is a phenomenon known as "precession" which necessitates an occasional reference to the wet compass and resetting of the gyro compass.

3. VOR or OMNI: This is a most important radio aid to navigation and forms the basis for most instrument flying in the United States. Scattered at appropriate positions around the country are these remarkable instruments which emit frequencies for each of the 360 points on the compass. In the modern aircraft a navigational aid is capable of receiving this electronic impulse and identifying the radial on the compass, signifying the current position of the aircraft vis-a-vis the OMNI on the ground. Although varying slightly in appearance, all OMNI receivers show compass headings and a small window which reads "off," "to," or "from." When the aircraft is within range of the OMNI—and this is largely conditioned by terrain and altitude—the needle on the face of the dial can be centered by turning the OMNI Bearing Selector (OBS). If flying toward the OMNI, the needle is centered with the "to" indicator in the window and pilot merely flies the heading indicated on the dial. Minor changes in heading will be needed contingent on the wind and the accuracy of his line of flight but a new and corrected heading is immediately available by merely centering the needle. As the pilot passes the navigation aid on the ground, the small window will show a switch from "to" to "from" and flight will continue with the needle again being centered as necessary. As the signal fades, the aircraft is usually in the territory of another OMNI on the route of flight and the same procedure is repeated. By virtue of the accuracy of this remarkable instrument one may find herself rapidly, if temporarily lost by merely tuning two OMNI's in the general area; centering the needles on each in the "from" position and drawing lines on the Sectional chart outbound from each OMNI on the indicated heading. At the intersection of these lines is the current location.

4. Localizer or Instrument Landing System (ILS): This is a "mini-OMNI" describing a much more precise and accurate pathway in the sky which must be flown by the pilot to keep the needle centered. As with the standard OMNI described above, there is a specific frequency and this should be checked by listening on the OMNI frequency for an identifying Morse code or vocal identification. "Flying the localizer" on final approach to an airport under instrument conditions is probably the most demanding job a pilot has to complete and tensions may be the highest during the performance of this task.

5. Glide slope: In many instrument landing systems a wedge-like area of altitude identifying the proper slope of flight to touch-down is incorporated. This will be reflected on the face of the OMNI by a horizontal bar that will rise above center when the aircraft is below the ideal slope and drop below the center when the

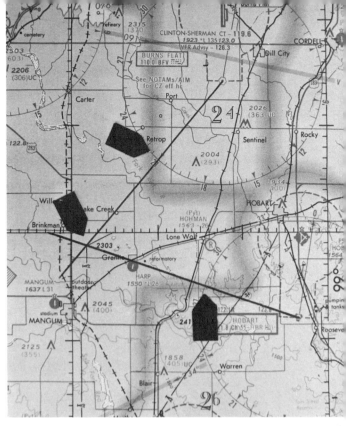

When the ground is not visible or there are no obvious landmarks to identify your position, the instruments can be of help. This depicts the technique of "triangulation" by centering the needles of your two VORs with the "From" indication showing in the window. Two nearby compass roses are used, with lines drawn through the center and the outbound heading shown on the instrument. Where they meet—there you are!

aircraft is above the theoretical ideal. With low ceilings the pilot has an added factor of safety when he flies the glide slope properly.

6. Three light marker: Many airports have an "outer marker" and a "middle marker" at specified distances from touch-down. These activate both visual (blue for the outer marker and amber for the middle marker) and audible (— —for the outer marker, and · — for the middle marker) signals when the aircraft traverses a specified point. In addition there is a third marker generally known as a "fan marker" or "Z marker" which is now rarely used as a navigational aid. This is signaled by activation of a white light and an audible signal which will usually be a series of dashes.

7. Distance measuring equipment (DME): This instrument will "read out" the distance to a navigational fix that has

"MY NEW BOYFRIEND TELLS ME THAT HE'S INSTRUMENT RATED, AND I DIDN'T EVEN KNOW HE LIKED MUSIC. ALL HE EVER DOES IS TALK ABOUT AIRPLANES."

been selected by turning to the appropriate frequency. The ultra-high frequency (UHF) radio beam is sent to the appropriate OMNI which must be one with TACAN capability. Such stations are identified in both Sectional and IFR charts. The signal sent by the aircraft is returned and time is electronically measured and graphically portrayed on a dial or by a direct digital read-out in nautical miles. It is to be remembered that the DME measures in:

a. nautical miles rather than statute miles, and

b. slant miles from the aircraft to the VORTAC, so altitude adds to the "across the ground" distance.

Most DME equipment will also give a direct read-out in ground speed expressed in nautical miles-per-hour. This may be helpful in selecting the altitude with the most favorable winds.

8. Automatic direction finder (ADF): This handy device doubles as a navigational aid, and radio to listen to the ball game on a long flight. Quite simply it is a radio receiver with an expanded range of frequencies which works by a rotating antenna that seeks the frequency tuned on the receiver. In parts of Mexico and other less aeronautically developed countries the ADF becomes the single most important electronic aid to navigation. Low frequency beacons emitting on a fixed frequency are inexpensive and easy to maintain; but should none be available in an area, a radio station can be tuned and the needle will point directly to the antenna in exactly the same way it does to the antenna of a low frequency beacon. The pilot simply turns the aircraft so that the arrow is at 0 degrees (right over the nose) and follows the arrow to the source of the signal.

9. Clock: It is hard to imagine that a simple clock is a navigational instrument, but it is of great importance during many aspects of flight. Gallons per hour, miles per hour, times recorded from one navigational fix to another, and the time allotted before having to execute a missed approach on an instrument landing are merely some examples where accurate recording of time is needed. A good wristwatch with a second hand will suffice but a stop watch mounted handily on the panel or yoke will prove to be a valuable addition. This is another area where the flying companion can be helpful. Clock readings can be jotted down when navigational points are reached, when gasoline tanks are changed, when the outer marker is passed, etc.

10. Transponder: This electronic device "paints" your aircraft's location on a radar screen. As described in "The Numbers Game" there are specific codes that mean specific things to the controller on the ground. You will hear the terms "squawk" and "ident." The former merely means turning the settings on the device to a new set of numbers, or code. The term "ident" involves actuating the ident button on the transponder which will cause your electronic image to "blossom" on the radarscope on the ground and verify your identity and location.

11. Weather radar: Only the most sophisticated general aviation aircraft have this device. Briefly stated, the radar portrays distant weather phenomena such as thunderstorms and heavy precipitation, giving the pilot a "track" he may fly to avoid these threats.

d. Radios: Important radio frequencies are discussed in "The Numbers Game" and will not be repeated here. The usual aircraft radio in a modern light airplane will be a part of a unit known as a NAV-COM and displayed near the VOR. The microphone will also plug into the panel and will have a switch that must be fully depressed for successful voice transmission. Since static may interfere with clear reception most radios have a "squelch" knob that can be rotated to an ideal point for maximum clarity. Care should be taken not to fully turn this knob as it can squelch everything with the erroneous conclusion that the radio is inoperative.

The Instrument Panel

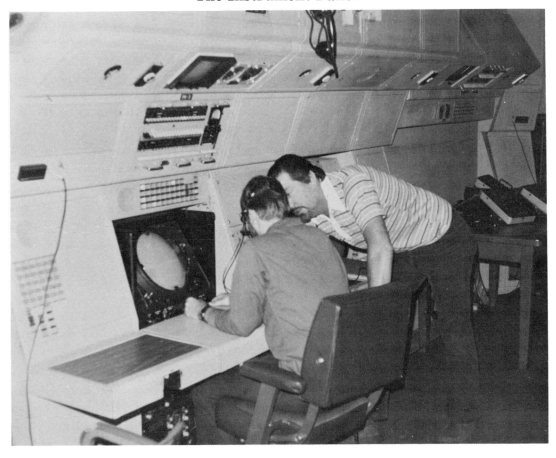

Controllers at one of the consoles in the Navy portion of "San Diego Radio" watching the progress of civilian and military aircraft on the radar screen.

Most panels also have a series of switches that will place various instruments on "stand-by." These must be correctly oriented to the "on" position or the speaker will remain mute. In the unlikely event of a radio failure remember that you may receive information on the ADF or VOR although there is no provision for voice transmission

e. Emergency gear: Emergency radio frequencies and transponder codes are listed in "The Numbers Game" and should be committed to memory. Since three are so important they will be listed here in addition:

121.5 on the aircraft radio to declare an emergency.

7700 on the transponder to declare an emergency.

7600 on the transponder to declare radio failure.

1. Emergency locator transmitter (ELT): This device is designed to locate a downed aircraft. Should it be clear that a forced landing is imminent the switch can be activated just before landing to ensure its functioning. The device emits a signal on the emergency frequency that can by "tracked" by other aircraft and direction finding equipment on the ground.

2. Emergency gear down equipment: This is of importance in aircraft with retractable landing gear. In the majority of such aircraft there will be a series of ways the pilot and his passenger will know that the gear is not in proper position. Lights will flash; the gear down lights will not be lighted, and an audible signal will be heard. In high wing aircraft the gear can be visually inspected from the windows, and in low wing twin engine planes a mirror on the engine compartment will reflect the nose gear. If the gear are dropped electrically, the breaker switches should be checked and reset if tripped. In any airplane there will be manual techniques to lower the wheels. In some airplanes with hydraulic systems a separate set of lines actuated by a carbon dioxide cylinder will be available for emergency use.

3. Stall warning indicator: Since a stall may be a hazardous thing, modern aircraft have both visible displays on the panel as well as an audible signal when a stall is approaching. A major part of the early training of every pilot relates to the avoidance of stalls and this emergency device will probably never be seen or heard in action.

4. Master switch: This becomes an emergency device only in case of a forced landing when it should be shut down before the landing is accomplished; or in the event of smoke or fire. If smoke in the cabin is evident or there is the smell of overheated electrical equipment, the Master switch should be turned off until the source has been identified. The engine will not stop when this is done so this need not be feared.

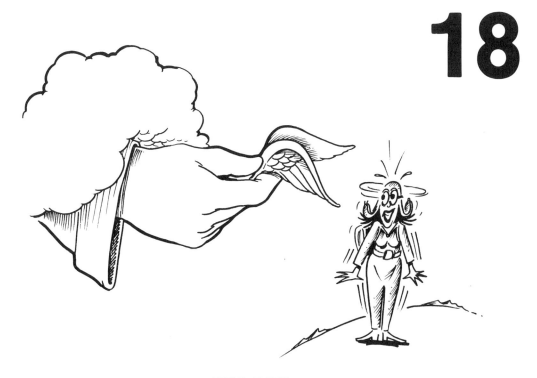

18

THE NOVITIATE CO-PILOT

The flying companion attains near "co-pilot" status when she has reached a point in her experience that she can assist her pilot in the preparation of a long cross-country flight involving both pilotage — her new area of expertise — and the use of instruments for navigation. The latter is primarily the province of the pilot, but on a long cross-country trip both modalities are necessary and are used. It is only under instrument conditions or when flying "VFR on top," where the ground is not visible, that pilotage is not a part of the navigation process.

America is a diverse, varied country in many ways; not the least of which is the topography. In spite of this, there are large parts of our country which show great variety in appearance to the traveller on the ground, but are monotonously the same when visualized from several thousand feet in the sky. There is a sameness in the huge areas of grain production in the Midwest where each rural town has its inevitable grain

elevators and outdoor theaters. There is a similar lack of identity, as seen from the air, in the broad expanses of range and oil producing country in west and central Texas. The forests and lakes of northern Michigan, Minnesota, and Wisconsin can also become confusing when the navigator, using pilotage techniques, begins to search for identifiable checkpoints.

Sharp eyes and constant attention to the ground passing below are tremendously important. However, in modern general aviation, pilotage has been beautifully supplemented by electronic navigational techniques. These are so excellent that they tend to lull the pilot into a sense of security that completely dissipates should an electrical failure occur.

As a consequence the team of pilot and newly initiated co-pilot work together. The pilot is primarily occupied with the technical aspects of flying the craft and using instruments such as the VOR (omni), DME (distance measuring

From White Knuckles to Cockpit Cool

equipment), and ADF (automatic direction finder) for navigation. The co-pilot uses eyes, charts, plotter, clock, and simple calculations of groundspeed to "backup" the information derived from the instruments.

This teamwork begins well in advance of the "walk around" and entry into the aircraft cabin. The pilot either calls the Flight Service Station or visits this office for information as to winds and weather. Maps and routes are studied together and the co-pilot places her emphasis on the "checkpoints" discussed in the earlier chapter. Her notes include the airport information of the home and destination airports. She will jot down such information as approach control frequencies, airport elevations, runway orientation and

length. She and the pilot consult with the air traffic specialist concerning recent Pireps (pilot reports), and NOTAMS (notices to airmen) to be sure that the weather is as predicted, and the various navigation aids are functioning.

Many airports have an ATIS (automatic terminal information service) frequency. The aircraft radio should be tuned to monitor this prior to starting the engine. Such information as wind velocity and direction, the active runway, taxi instructions, and the current altimeter setting are included.

Once the engine is started the pilot will tune the radio to the ground frequency and announce his readiness to taxi to his takeoff site. The co-pilot should be ready with this radio frequency in the event the

Tower personnel manning the Ground Control monitor and direct the movement of all aircraft off of the runways. Your pilot may not legally taxi without clearance from the controller with this responsibility. A collision on the runway can be just as serious as one in the air!

The Novitiate Co-Pilot

In a "controlled" airport, a tower will be found at some point on the field. Its location can be found on the approach plate, but since it usually dominates the airport area, it can be quickly spotted. Here are the men and women responsible for your safety as you depart the airport or prepare for landing. They are ever watchful and are there for the sole reason of protecting your lives and those of others using that particular field. As you become more proficient and more interested, a courteous call to the tower supervisor often will allow you to enter the tower and watch these specialists in action. It is impressive.

pilot does not immediately have it at his fingertips.

At the run-up area the pilot has many responsibilities confirming the flightworthiness of his aircraft. Prior to departure the radio will be changed from ground to tower frequency, and this number should be in the information list prepared by the co-pilot. In a "controlled" airport — one with a tower — the pilot will declare his readiness for takeoff and will then be cleared to start his journey. In an "uncontrolled" airport, there will be neither a ground nor a tower frequency, and the Unicom frequency of 122.8 will be tuned prior to entering the taxi-way. At such an airport, vigilance must be at least doubled as it is the sole responsibility of the pilot to decide when he should taxi onto the runway and begin his takeoff run. When there is more than one runway at such an airport, he must judge by his analysis of the wind direction which runway he will use. Both pilot and co-pilot should very, very carefully scrutinize the skies in every direction before taxiing into takeoff position. It is sad to relate, but there are often careless pilots who do not go through the formality of the routinized "pattern" prior to landing at an uncontrolled airport. Hence, it is every man (or woman) for himself!!!!

Before the actual takeoff the co-pilot has another opportunity to be useful.

Every careful pilot uses a check-list during the run-up phase in advance of actually taxiing onto the active runway. This is usually placarded on the sunvisor or panel, but may be typed on a card. In any event, it is helpful to call out the various items that must be checked, allowing the pilot to concentrate on the procedures. This will prevent accidental skipping over a check-list item. It is during the run-up that such things as the performance of the flaps, magnetos, alternator, ailerons, elevators, etc., are tested. It is also at this time that the gyro compass is carefully set by reference to the wet compass, and a quick survey of all of the engine and flight instruments is made.

The trip we will now take together is an ambitious one. We will combine the new skills of the co-pilot with the licensed accomplishments of the pilot. The route will begin in Lubbock, Texas; then proceed to Abilene; to Dallas; north to Wichita Falls; and west again to Lubbock. Landings at Dallas and Wichita Falls will be made en route. The emphasis will be placed on the necessity for teamwork between the pilot and novitiate co-pilot!

The route poses many challenges to both flying participants. It also offers the advantage of the use of a single Sectional chart; the Dallas-Fort Worth Sectional. This makes flight planning more pleasant, and descriptive material easier to visualize.

The trip involves pilotage over areas of seemingly featureless terrain. Several major cities including one Terminal Control Area, are crossed. There are long distances between VOR's. Intersections of airways make up part of the flight plan.

Although the accompanying photographs of charts will identify many check-points, the use of an actual Sectional chart is necessary for the measurements. The primary emphasis will be on pilotage, but navigational techniques using instruments will be described in limited detail. The latter need not be learned, but their understanding makes the trip more interesting.

The flight plan will be filed in this way: Victor 62, Abilene; Victor 16, Dallas Greater Southwest; Direct, Love Field; Landing, Love Field. The second leg will be as follows: Dallas, Love Field, Direct, Sange Intersection; Victor 358, Lake Kiowa Intersection; Victor 114, Wichita Falls; Landing, Wichita Falls Municipal Airport. The third, and terminal leg of the flight will be described: Wichita Falls Municipal, Victor 102; landing Lubbock Regional Airport.

Prior to takeoff, the pilot will set his navigational omni to coincide with the heading from Lubbock to Abilene. The chart shows this to be a magnetic heading of 114 degrees. Because the distance from Lubbock to Abilene is great, the pilot will initially track "outbound" using the Lubbock VOR frequency of 110.8. The omni heading will be set to 114 degrees, and as the course is established, the visual display in the omni "window" will show a "From" designation. This indicates that the pilot is on an outbound course from Lubbock, using the Lubbock VOR. So long as the omni needle is centered, he can assume that he is faithfully tracking on his planned 114 degree heading. If the needle drifts to the right, it means that he has drifted off course to the left, and a turn to the right will re-establish a proper track. About half way between Lubbock and Abilene, he will change from the Lubbock VOR to the Abilene VOR with its frequency of 113.7. At that time the omni will show a change from the "From" designation to a "To" signal, indicating that he is now on a course **to** Abilene. No other significant electronic navigational aids exist in the long segment between Lubbock and Abilene. Even if the aircraft

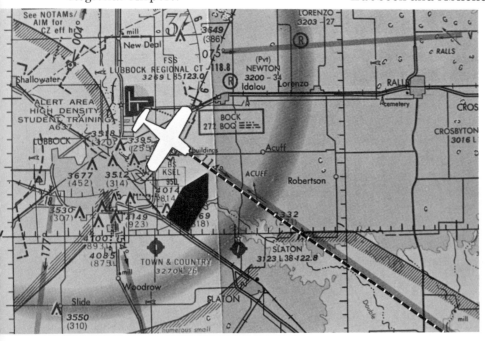

The 114° heading on the Sectional Chart corresponds to the 114° reading on the OMNI face.

is equipped with a radar transponder, the ability of the Lubbock and Abilene Flight Service Stations to track your craft by radar is exceeded.

Your job of pilotage begins immediately after takeoff. To your right the city of Lubbock will be seen, and shortly thereafter you will cross a large dual highway and soon see a series of small lakes off the right wing. The city of Slaton with a single runway airport north and west of the town center makes your next excellent landmark. At about this point, the discriminating eye will note a definite change in topography as there is a rather sharp drop in ground elevation, designated by the change in color on the map. A large north-south highway is next crossed and following this, a wash will appear with a bridge almost directly under your flight path. Another bridge may be seen a few miles further to the left. At about this point in the flight the city of Post should be visible over the right wing, with a small airport featuring two short runways visible slightly to the north and east. The sinuous river called the Double Mountain Fork should then come into view. Depending on the timing of recent rains it may be an actual river or a dry wash, but will be visible. If properly on course you should cross two roads and see a bridge on the left of the plane just at the time your flight arrives over Double Mountain Fork. Further to the left is a cluster of buildings and objects that may be identified as a school, pumping station, and oil tanks. Your course takes you directly over the city of Rotan with a single runway airport to the southeast; a tower to the left, and a cement plant to the right. Ten miles further along your course the small city of Hamlin with a single runway airport can be seen off the left wing. At this point the city of Abilene will probably be visible in the distance.

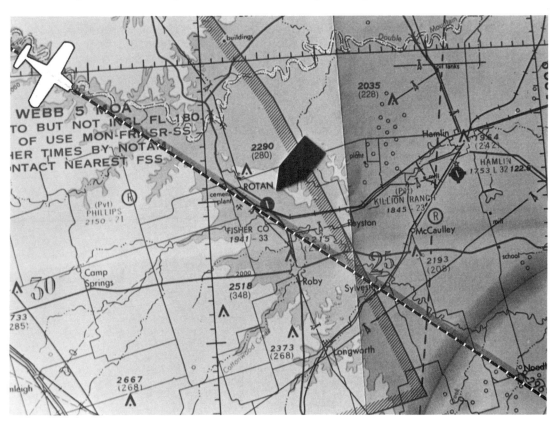

The airport at Rotan is surrounded by numerous, easily identified, check points.

Dyess Air Force Base, with its long runway is an excellent check point.

The size of this city makes it definite, but there are abundant landmarks which should be searched for simply for practice. These should include Dyess Air Force Base with a long, single runway to the right. You will cross this just as your pilot notes a change in his omni reading from "To" to "From" indicating passage over the VOR. A lake with a dam at its northern end is also to the right of the course. Just past this body of water, the multi-runway Abilene County Airport is seen, south and east of the body of the city of Abilene.

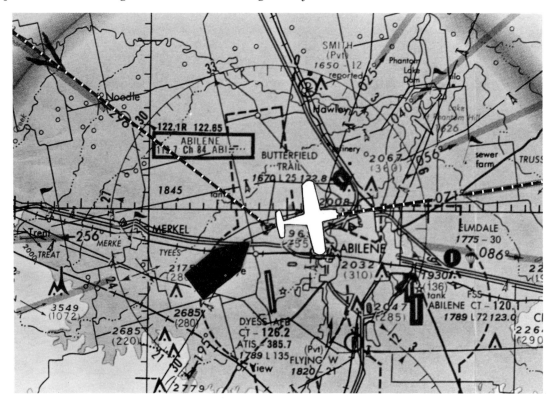

Abilene area is pictured here. The arrow points to the Abilene VOR. You should also note the heading change to 071°.

The arrow indicates the box containing the information for the Mineral Wells ADF. First the name: MINERAL WELLS; second, the number to be dialed into the ADF receiver: 266; and third, the Morse Code information MWL (—— ·—— ·—··). You will observe that the signal device is located on the airport as can be seen by the burst of dots.

At the Abilene VOR the heading changes to 071 degrees, and a gentle left turn will occur. As before, your pilot will continue to track on the Abilene VOR, keeping the needle centered, but with the new heading of 071 degrees entered in place of the earlier 114 degree heading. Between Dallas and Abilene, the Millsap VOR appears, with a frequency of 117.7. About half way between Abilene and Mineral Wells, your pilot will change to this frequency and the "From" Abilene reading will give way to a "To" Millsap indication.

The chart will show a series of red dots radiating around the Mineral Wells Airport. A magenta box nearby gives the legend: Mineral Wells, and the figure **266**, with a Morse Code identification for MWL. If your airplane is equipped with an ADF, tuning this to 266 and listening for the proper Morse Code signal will identify this navigation aid. The ADF needle will point directly to the beacon located at the Mineral Wells Airport, thus giving you further electronic proof of the accuracy of your navigation.

At Millsap VOR, passage over the VOR housing on the ground below will cause a swing in the indicator from "To" to "From." A slight bend in the airway to 074 degrees will mean a minute heading change by your pilot as he tracks toward his landing at Dallas Love Field.

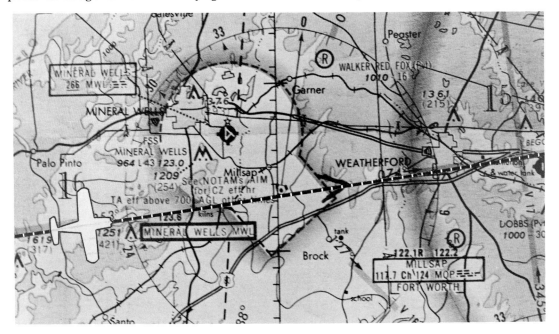

At the Millsap VOR there is a slight heading change to 074°. The freeway becomes a good continuing reference.

The heavy circle designates the Dallas-Fort Worth Terminal Control Area (TCA). This is an area of high aircraft density and special rules apply to entering this airspace. The arrow identifies Lake Grapevine, northwest of the huge Dallas-Fort Worth airport. Love Field is seen to the eastern side of the TCA with TANK low frequency beacon just southeast of the field.

Before returning to your job of pilotage, a brief mention of the TCA (Terminal Control Area) is needed. Although you have planned a clearly defined pathway through the sky to Dallas Greater Southwest VOR, and then on to Love Field, the pragmatics of air traffic will result in a change in your plans. A large circle defining the limits of the Dallas-Fort Worth TCA is seen on the chart. Prior to entering this airspace your pilot will make a radio call to a frequency specified on the TCA chart, identifying his position and intentions. This frequency is also available through the Dallas-Fort Worth ATIS, on the Sectional chart, through the nearby Flight Service Stations, as well as on the special TCA chart. Since your flight will end with a landing at Love Field, your pilot will notify Approach Control and he will be directed (vectored) to a position that will allow him to both make his landing at Love Field, and avoid the heavy concentration of aircraft that regularly populate the Dallas-Fort Worth area. As described elsewhere, you will need to be ready with the landing information about Love Field including the radio frequencies for ATIS, Tower and Ground controls. The altitude of 487 feet should have been recorded from the chart earlier so that it is on the tip of your tongue. Your pilot will be "handed off" by the Dallas controller to the Love Field tower just before landing. This series of direction, altitude, and radio frequency changes may become hectic so "back up" help will be appreciated.

The above digression does not mean that you are to sleep or read a novel during the leg between Abilene and the edge

The Novitiate Co-Pilot

of the Dallas-Fort Worth TCA. This segment must be made accurately and safely and a radio or transponder failure could immediately place you in the navigational "driver's seat" with the position information so vital to the pilot.

You will have a chance to exercise one other skill the co-pilot should ultimately master with additional flying. Although described in detail elsewhere one simple problem relating to this flight using the aviation computer will be described. This involves use of the computer to solve a "time and distance" problem. The segment of the trip between Abilene and Millsap VOR contains several good check-points, and one of the best appears at exactly 35 nautical miles after passing over the Abilene VOR. At the exact time the passage over the VOR is signaled by the change to "From" to "To," note down the exact time on a sheet of notepaper, or write it directly on the Sectional chart. When you pass the large road leading to Breckenridge, with the multi-runway Stephen County Airport to the southeast of the city, and with the large body of water containing a dam at its northern end, again note the exact time.

You now have two important pieces of information, i.e. 35 nautical miles, and the time it took to traverse that distance. For purposes of simplicity we will assume that the time was exactly 20 minutes. You can now solve a simple arithmetical problem with the computer and obtain the speed over the ground your aircraft is making. Although such a problem can be answered by simple arithmetical means, most pilots prefer the handy aviation computer. This problem is speedily solved by placing the number 35 on the "miles" scale exactly opposite to the number 20 on the "minutes" scale. Look over to the arrow and it will be found reposing exactly on the number 10.5. You have only one thing to remember at this point, and that is that a zero has to be added to the result; hence 10.5 becomes 105 nautical miles per hour. Without changing

anything you can now solve the time it will take to reach any check-point further along your path. Assuming no material change in power settings by your pilot, or wind speed and direction, you can quickly measure with your plotter the distance to the edge of the Dallas-Fort Worth TCA and find that it is 76 nautical miles further along your route. Look again at the computer and find 76 on the "miles" scale. Directly across from it will be the number 43.5—the number of minutes it will take to reach the border of the TCA.

Pilotage on the Abilene to Dallas segment starts with the city of Abilene on your right, a few moments after you cross the Abilene VOR. Shortly thereafter, you pass a sharply bending road leading to the town of Albany, which can be seen off the left wing. Albany is further identified by a small airport with a single runway. Immediately after seeing Albany, large Lake Breckenridge is seen on the left, and after that the road we have used for our computer problem. If there is doubt about Breckenridge because of clouds or fog and the aircraft has an ADF, it can be tuned to 245. The Morse Code identification of BKD is then confirmed and the ADF needle should swing promptly to the left, pointing directly at the city. Beyond Breckenridge and again on the left, the Possum Kingdom Lake with many fingers and extensions in multiple directions is viewed. By this time a large freeway should be visible on the right, merging slowly in the direction of your course. On your right, and close to your course line, a smaller lake with a triangular shape and a dam at the eastern end can be seen.

Just prior to reaching the Millsap VOR the city of Mineral Wells is viewed to the left, with an ADF beacon and the frequency of 266 can be checked. Mineral Wells has a Flight Service Station, and updated weather and route information as well as a current altimeter setting can be obtained by a radio call to this facility.

A moment or two after passing Mineral Wells, the Millsap VOR will swing from

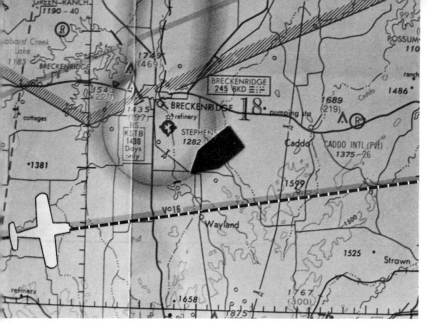

South of Breckenridge Victor 16 crosses the highway used in the computer problem. The sequence of a small lake with an island and a dam at its northern end with a multi-runway airport just north, and huge Lake Breckenridge northwest make pilotage in this area easy.

"To" to "From," and a slight heading change to 074 degrees will be made by the pilot. Weatherford now lies directly ahead with two freeways forming a triangle and merging about 3 nautical miles from the eastern edge of the city. Parker County Airport, with a single runway is also at this point and practically on your course line.

At about the area of Meacham County Airport, your pilot will change his omni to the Greater Southwest VOR, with a frequency of 113.1, and the panel will show a "To" heading. Entering the TCA your aircraft will come under "positive" control by air traffic specialists. When you cross the Greater Southwest VOR, the omni will shift from "To" to "From" and

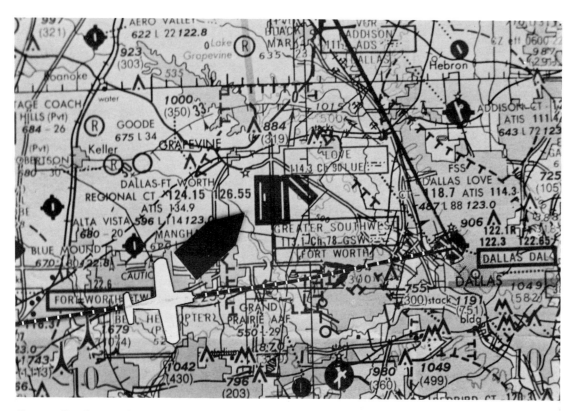

Greater Southwest Airport and Love Field lie side by side. Notice that the runways have somewhat similar orientation, but Lake Grapevine is nearer Greater Southwest and a freeway is shown running between the two long runways at this field.

While it is possible to read the radio information and check points on a regular Sectional Chart as shown in this photograph, it is wise to have the more detailed Terminal Control Area Chart.

both the gigantic Dallas-Fort Worth Regional Airport to your left, and Love Field directly ahead, should be visible. Depending on the degree of control exercised by the air controller, your pilot may wish to tune the Love Field VOR with a frequency change to 114.3. Further confirmation of his location can be obtained by tuning the ADF to Tank beacon, with a frequency of 388, and a Morse Code identification of DDA. This lies just southeast of Love Field. When the pilot is "handed off" to the Love Field tower, landing follows immediately.

With the first leg completed, preparations must be made for the flight segment to Wichita Falls. The usual routine of fueling, packing, checking weather and wind information must be repeated. The "walk around" is duplicated, and all of the necessary radio

frequencies are recorded. Since your takeoff originates within the TCA, your pilot will undoubtedly again be vectored for the initial 10 to 20 miles of the flight in order to avoid the heavy traffic coming from nearby Dallas-Fort Worth Regional Airport. Using the "slide over" technique with your plotter as a straight-edge, you can quickly note that your approximate heading to join Victor 358 will be about 325 degrees. Here your pilot will join the airway at Sange intersection. A digression is necessary to discuss the technique your pilot uses to find one of these designated "intersections in the sky." You will note on the chart that the heading of Victor 358 outbound from Greater Southwest is 347 degrees. Your pilot will enter the VOR frequency for Greater Southwest, which we have noted earlier is 113.1 Since he will be east (to the right) of Victor 358,

101

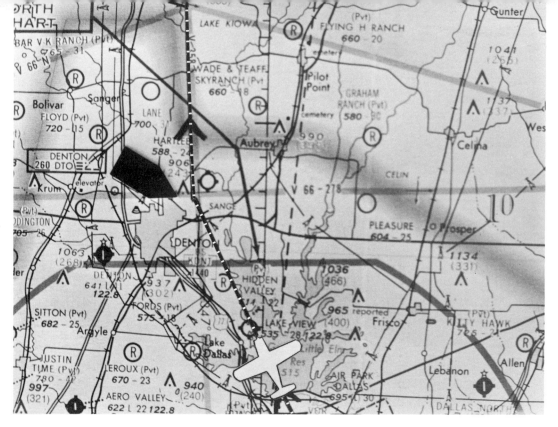

Sange intersection is at the north side of the town of Denton. The intersection is where V66-278 crosses V358.

the needle on the omni on the panel will swing widely to the left, indicating a "fly left" to reach Victor 358.

You will also note that the other airway making up Sange intersection is Victor 66. Looking to the right, or east of the intersection, you will find the Blue Ridge VOR. This is designated on the chart by the characteristic "compass rose" and is 36 nautical miles away. The frequency for this VOR is 114.9, and the outbound heading to Sange intersection is 260 degrees. If the airplane has a second navigation receiver, the omni can be preset to this heading. Since you are south, and therefore to the left of the Blue Ridge 260 degree radial, that needle will swing widely to the right, indicating a "fly right" command to reach 260 degrees.

Your pilot, after takeoff, will fly according to the commands emanating from Departure Control until he is released to "resume normal navigation." At that time he will fly in the general direction of Sange intersection as determined by your original calculation of the heading. When both omni needles have centered he will know that he is now safely established on

Victor 358, and is exactly at Sange intersection. Should Blue Ridge VOR be inoperative, or give a weak signal, the pilot can cross-check by tuning the Bridgeport VOR to the west. This has a frequency of 116.5, and by rotating the dial to an outbound heading of 078 degrees a centered needle confirms Victor 66 and Sange intersection.

As you leave Love Field there are a host of landmarks that make pilotage easy. Dallas-Fort Worth Regional Airport is on the left with Lake Grapevine slanting to the northwest. Directly along your course is the huge Garza Reservoir, with the city of Denton at its northwest terminus. A large freeway between Dallas and Denton roughly parallels your course to Sange intersection.

The next segment is short and takes you to Kiowa intersection. This "crossroad" is made up of the 347 degree outbound heading from Greater Southwest, and the 277 degree heading from Blue Ridge. Attainment of this position is signified by the centering of the omni needles.

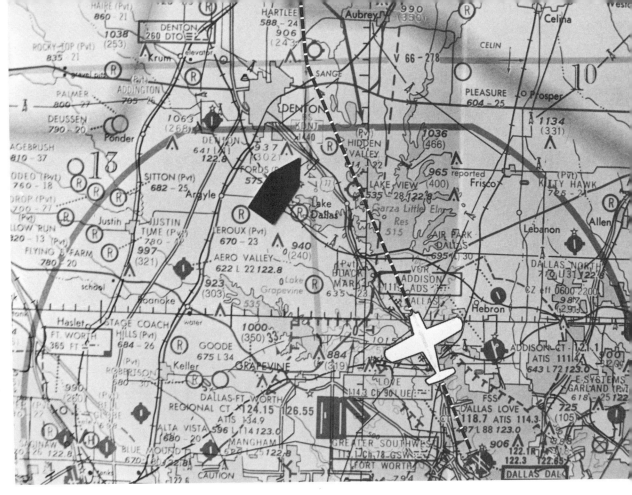

Pilotage is a pleasure north of Dallas, as check points abound. A large freeway to Denton, with a railroad to the east and Garza Reservoir further to the east are seen just prior to reaching Sange Intersection. This is still in the TCA and your pilot will probably be vectored, which will mean that you will have to keep a sharp eye to be able to assist him in locating himself when he is told to "resume normal navigation."

* * *

Lake Kiowa intersection is the crossing of V114-66N and V358. Pilotage check points are discussed in the written material.

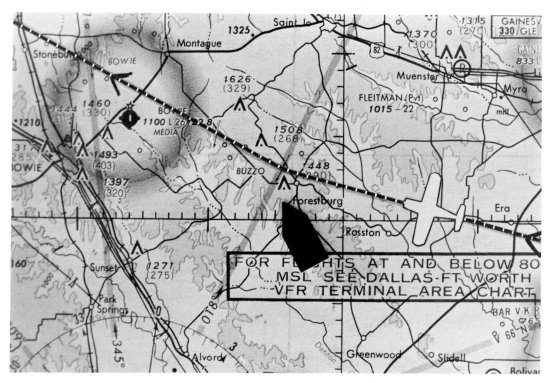

Buzzo intersection is the next slight change in direction. At this point V161-163 cross V114. As you can see from these slight changes in direction, it is important to follow visual check points carefully.

You have now reached the point where you join Victor 66 North with its co-designation of Victor 114. Your pilot makes a heading change to 277 degrees, meaning a rather sharp left turn. Buzzo intersection is 25 miles west of Kiowa intersection. It is made up of the 277 degree outbound heading from Blue Ridge — the route you are now flying — and the 018 degree outbound heading from Bridgeport VOR. A very subtle change in course to the north will be made by your pilot when the omni needles center and confirm your arrival at Buzzo intersection.

Visual landmarks on the leg between Kiowa intersection and Wichita Falls begin with a large north-south freeway heading into the city of Gainesville, off the right wing. Two large freeways cross just west of Gainesville. Slightly further to the west a multi-runway airport, with an ADF frequency of 330 and a Morse Code identification of GLE, appears. North of Gainesville a sinuous river and a

lake with a dam at the eastern end can be seen if the weather is clear. Bodies of water often reflect sunlight and can be identified from great distances, so the fact that these landmarks exceed 15 miles is of reduced significance. The small towns of Muenster, Saint Lo, and Nocona appear on your right at nearly equidistant intervals. Saint Lo is identified by two bodies of water, one to the southeast with a small dam at its southern end, and the other just north of the town. Nocona has a single runway airport southwest of town. Bowie Airport, another single runway airport, is slightly over a mile to the left of your track. By this time a large freeway merging in a northwest direction from Fort Worth to Wichita Falls will be seen on the left. At Henrietta you join this freeway preparatory to your landing at Wichita Falls Municipal Airport.

Your chart shows this airport to be directly north of the population center of Wichita Falls. It also indicates that the Wichita Falls VOR, with a frequency of

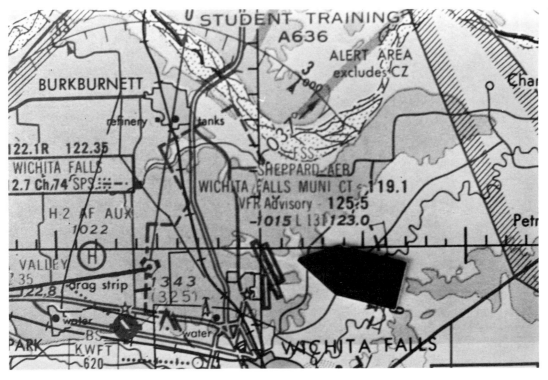

Wichita Falls Airport location with necessary radio and landing information.

112.7, is four miles due west of your destination. Probably the best identifications from a purely pilotage standpoint are the due north location of the airport, and its position east of a whole complex of large freeways that interlace immediately north of the city.

Your chart signifies a "VFR Advisory" frequency of 125.5, and this should be tuned on the aircraft radio for VFR information. Contact with the tower after following the VFR Advisory directions will confirm landing instructions. Your chart shows an altitude of 1015 feet, so your pilot will make his pattern at 1815 feet unless otherwise directed by the controller in the Wichita Falls tower.

Takeoff from Wichita Falls duplicates other takeoffs — with all of the usual precautions followed! You are now on the leg home to Lubbock. Your heading from the Wichita Falls airport will be due west (270 degrees) to the VOR. Upon reaching the VOR an outbound heading of 252 degrees will establish you on Victor 102 and Victor 114 South.

Eight nautical miles from Wichita Falls VOR a small lake will be seen off of your right wing, with a dam at the southern end. Beyond this and on your left two large lakes, Lake Diversion and Lake Kemp, will appear. These have distinctive shapes and should make superb check points. Lake Diversion has the additional features of a dam at the northeastern end, and a single runway airport just a mile east of the dam.

Passing through the Wichita Falls area, you will note that your chart designates that as an "Alert Area" with a numerical designation of A-636. On the informational portion of the chart there is a legend indicating that this area has military flying activity from ground level to 4000 feet from Monday to Friday, starting at 7:00 a.m. and ending at 11:00 p.m. (0700-2300). This is merely a warning to you and your pilot to be particularly cautious to scan the skies diligently as you descend for landing, and climb out following takeoff. If desired, the degree of flying activity by the Air Force can be

Wichita Falls Municipal is located in an Alert Area. It is especially important to have all landing information written down before arrival. "Eyes outside the plane at all times!"

checked by a call to Sheppard Air Force Base on a frequency of 125.5.

In west and central Texas, as well as in other areas in the United States, the appearance on the chart of a body of water can be erroneous. During dry seasons shallow lakes may evaporate. Large bodies of water or those with dams are less likely to fade away, and are better check-points.

Between Lake Kemp and the Guthrie VOR, landmarks become very scarce. When the needle on the omni tuned to Guthrie VOR (112.4) swings slightly and the designation goes from "To" to "From," you can confirm your position by noting your passage over a large north-south road, with a small airport 9 miles off of your left wing. Your practiced eye now may be able to pick up gentle

Near Guthrie VOR the terrain is rather featureless, and noting the "X" formed by improved roads with the 6666 Ranch airport offers your main chance of maintaining your location by pilotage alone.

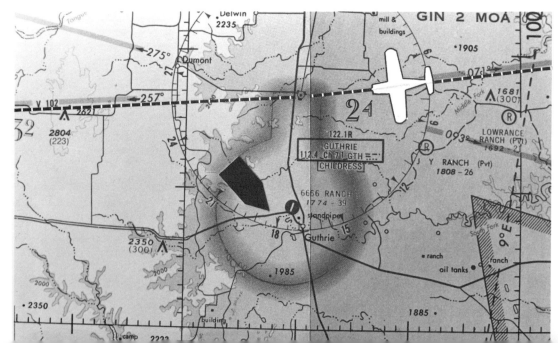

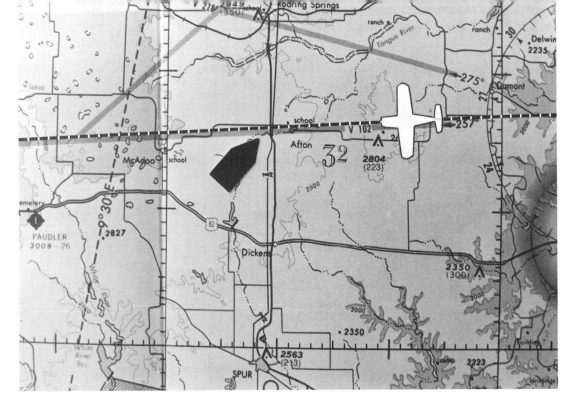

A friendly freeway roughly parallels your course in the "flat" country to the west. Victor 102 lies considerably north of Spur, but in clear west Texas skies the town of Spur, the freeway, and the lake with a dam at the southeastern end should give the information you need.

nuances in terrain, as you are now noting a slow increase in ground elevation after you pass Guthrie. "To" Guthrie, you have been on a magnetic heading of 252 degrees. "From" Guthrie to Lubbock, you deviate slightly to a new heading of 257 degrees on your outbound track.

Roughly paralleling your course on the left, you will see a large freeway and will cross an improved north-south road leading to Roaring Springs on the right of course, and Dickens on the left. A powerline with a series of pylons follows

this north-south road and will ease its identification. Three miles further west along the freeway another body of water with a dam at the southeastern end, is seen on the left. Crosbytown also lies on your left a few miles further along the route. It can be identified by two airports to the southeast and south, as well as a cemetery which may be visible adjacent to the highway. The town of Ralls is next seen on the left, and is easily identified by virtue of two freeways making a right angle west of town.

The last leg of your trip will follow the freeway passing through the towns of Ralls and Idalou.

From White Knuckles to Cockpit Cool

By this time the large city of Lubbock should be visible in the distance, and the omni setting should have been changed to 110.8; the Lubbock VOR frequency. A "To" designation will now appear in the omni window.

Lubbock Regional Airport lies to the north of the city and east of the Alert Area that surrounds Reese Air Force Base. In addition to its location north of the city and southeast of the VOR, an ADF beacon with a frequency of 272 and a Morse Code identification of BOQ, is on the airport. The rising terrain is confirmed by your noting the airport elevation of 3269 feet. Lubbock Approach Control, which your pilot will have contacted about the time you were passing Ralls, will hand you off to the Lubbock tower and your ambitious journey will safely end with the usual smooth landing!

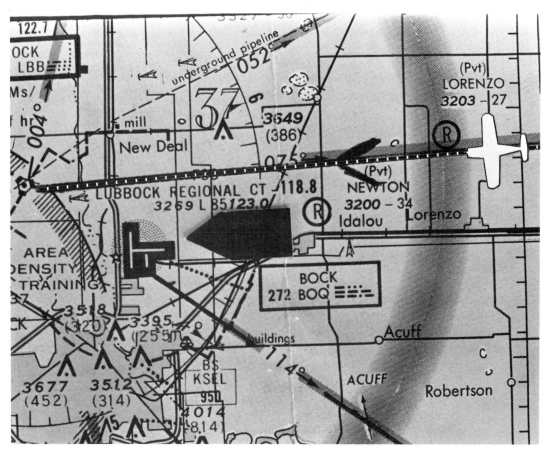

Lubbock Regional showing necessary landing information. Notice that an ADF is located on the field. This is always a comfort to know.

So! It never rains in New Mexico in July!

WEATHER AND TURBULENCE

Roswell, New Mexico was a place it never rained in summer for more than one afternoon at a time I assured my pilot as we sloshed through rivers of water toward our motel in the usually dry New Mexico city. Having grown up in west Texas, I felt confident that my prediction of the July 2nd weather in this part of the country would be accurate. I was sure that we had been wise in listening to the FAA briefer who had felt that neither Pinon VOR nor routes to the east or west of it were places to be flying with three of our children in a single engine plane.

A wet July 2nd came and went and the outlines of the trees were only vaguely visible through the rain and fog on July 3rd. Possible "breaks in the overcast" predicted for the following day proved funnels of water to drown out the usually brilliant July 4th fireworks display in Roswell.

The "go" or "no go" decision is basically at the discretion of the pilot, but a truly informed passenger can have valuable in-

put. In this case, my advice was "right" for all of the "wrong" reasons. Every possible reliable source of information should be tapped before the flight plan is filed. Constant recognition of the uncertainties of weather forecasting must also enter the decision-making process and other priorities (such as stretching of credit card limits) should not be major determinants in the final decision.

General axioms to be recognized are these:

1. Flight into adverse weather conditions is reponsible for a high percentage of aviation accidents.

2. Weather forecasting remains an uncertain science.

3. Weather conditions change rapidly and awaiting improving trends may be only a matter of minutes or hours (Roswell notwithstanding!).

4. In general, a weather briefer will respond only to the problem or question presented to him. Unless asked specifically many briefers will not volunteer a full

weather briefing or discuss alternate routes. If more help is needed or doubt remains, be sure your pilot is definitive in his request to the briefer.

5. Other means of transportation, although inconvenient and costly, may be cheapest in the long run.

6. A judicious "180 degree turn" in the face of unexpected weather problems often is a sign of bravery and not of cowardice!

When reflecting on this last axiom and our flying career in general, it seems that El Paso and its environs figures prominently. I can remember a 400 mile flight from El Paso to—El Paso, with no intermediate stops! This 180 degree turn took real fortitude as a Navy dinner with my husband at the speaker's table was being held in Phoenix that evening. By taking off a few hours later and "trying it again" we were able to meet the commitment even though it meant struggling into evening clothes in a restroom at the Phoenix Sky Harbor.

It is not the purpose of this chapter to make an amateur meteorologist of you. Familiarity with the sources of weather information and some general understanding of the terms used by forecasters as well as some of the major weather hazards will give you an appreciation of the need for thoughtful decision on the part of your pilot.

The sky is described as "clear" if there is less than one-tenth obscuration by

This pass looks innocent enough and there seems to be a hint of clearing in the "V" between the mountains. Actually, that "clearing" represents the color change of another mountain—so gaining altitude to clear these clouds is not only legal, but sensible.

cloud cover. It is said to be "scattered" if one-tenth to less than six-tenths of the sky is obscured. The term "broken" indicates six-tenths to nine-tenths of the sky covered. The forecaster will often describe the sky as obscured, but use the modifying phrase "breaks in the overcast" to indicate that a technically "overcast" sky may still offer the pilot the opportunity to find holes through which he may safely descend without actually penetrating cloud formations.

Dew point, the point at which condensation will occur, and temperature in Fahrenheit are always part of a full weather briefing. If these numbers are within three to five points of each other, fog may be anticipated.

Fortunately, in most planes the outside air temperature thermometer is easily seen from the right seat. It takes no special training to cast a jaundiced eye at this little circle to be sure that the magic number 32 degrees Fahrenheit or 0 degrees Celsius has not been reached. If you are in clear air, let it go merrily down

as you reach for the heater button; but in fog, rain, or clouds notify the pilot that he is approaching one jackpot he'd just as soon leave to somebody else—32 degrees Fahrenheit! This is the "freezing level" mentioned by the weather forecaster. One word to the wise: when the briefer has given your pilot the altitude at which freezing will occur it is important to note if your landing will take you through fog, rain, or clouds at that altitude. You will pick up ice on the wings or prop should this occur.

The wind at various altitudes and the altimeter setting as well as any "sigmet" or "airmet" advisories are also part of the briefing. "Sigmet" stands for "significant meteorological advisory" and is always to be heeded. These usually describe severe weather conditions hazardous to all aircraft. The "airmet" is an "advisory for light aircraft" and relates specifically to general aviation. My own private code for these is **S**top **I**n **G**ood **M**otel **E**arly **T**onight, and **A**lways **I**nsist **R**each **M**otel **E**arly **T**onight. If either a "sigmet" or an

"airmet" is in force in your area or along your intended route, be a believer!

If you accompany a pilot into a Flight Service Station you will be introduced to Aviation Weather Reports, and learn to read "sequence reports." This is coded information from hundreds of reporting stations and contains the description of weather and sky conditions as reported from each station at specified intervals. Included may be "Pireps," a contraction for "Pilot Reports." These are excellent to have, because they come from the lips of someone who has "been there." Weather maps will also be available with frontal activity and other significant weather information. Radar reports of precipitation and thunderstorm activity may be available. In the contiguous United States there are now in excess of 140 radar sites and many Flight Service Stations have repeater-scopes that will copy these displays and allow specialists to interpret them for the pilot, with you as an interested observer.

Regular weather forecasts are broadcast to pilots on request and include: terminal forecasts issued three times daily; area forecasts prepared twice daily; and 12 and 18 hour route forecasts that are detailed in nature and cover weather along a route 25 miles to each side of specific airways. These are issued three times daily. Winds and temperatures aloft are also forecasted on request.

Probably the most specific information is supplied by the En Route Flight Advisory Service. This relatively new and fantastic service covers much of the United States, and is expected to be more widespread in the future. By tuning 122.0 on the aviation radio, direct conversation with the forecaster having access to all available weather information sources, including voice contact with many pilots and direct telephonic communication with many reports, will give the pilot the most current possible information. This is a "two way street" and the forecaster will undoubtedly quiz your pilot about sky and wind conditions in your area so that he may be helpful to the next supplicant for weather advice.

Weather and Turbulence

U.S. Weather Broadcasts are transmitted at 15 minutes after the hour on most continuously functioning FAA radio ranges including the VOR as well as radio beacons having voice capability. These generally give a picture of weather within 150 miles of the source, and can be tuned for confirmation during flight. Weather briefers are not permitted to give you the unscientific observation of "eyeballing it." It is great to be able to add this to your total information. Many are the times a friend with whom we had not visited in many years has received an unexpected telephone call with a strange request to go out and take a look at the sky and tell us what he sees. It is an automatic reflex for relatives who know we are en route to their area to take a look "in all quadrants" before they answer the telephone. In summary, there are many sources of information but no wizard to make the final decision with respect to the safety of flight. Your informed observations can be a help.

Things are going smoothly. You are (at the intellectual level) convinced that flight is safe and fun. Then it happens— the bump in the road! There is a sudden re-evaluation of the wisdom of flying. Both literally and figuratively you feel that the "bottom has fallen out of the air." This is a respectable evaluation of turbulence and has foundation in your fundamental instincts. One of the truly inherited fears is the fear of falling or dropping, and it takes many years and much convincing to feel safe when the air suddenly becomes unstable and the ride rough and bouncy.

Turbulence is a warning and should be heeded by the pilot. Nevertheless, there are forms of turbulence that are merely inconvenient and have no reflection on the safety of flight. This is best exemplified by the choppiness you feel when flying over uneven terrain where wind currents, like waves of the ocean, become disturbed by interruption of smooth flow over the uneven ground

SMOOTH FLIGHT ABOVE CLOUDS

BUMPY FLIGHT BELOW CLOUDS

which they traverse. Another form that is of little significance except as a bother is that arising from varying degrees of convection ascending from the heat absorbing or reflecting characteristics of the ground below. On a hot day convection currents rise to great heights and will affect the smoothness of flight. If the ground surface reflects heat well, such as large areas of paving or smooth ground, the currents will rise rapidly and chop will be distinct. Conversely, terrain covered by crops or trees will absorb heat well and less will be reflected, resulting in a smoother ride. The same is true of large bodies of water. During the day these are colder than the land and less convection will occur over water. At night, however, the water may be warmer as the land cools and the opposite prevails. On a hot day the pilot can expect, and you will observe, that the plane may "float" as the concrete runway is reached. This is simply another evidence of the reflected heat rising from the paving with a slowing of the "rate of sink" of the aircraft.

Turbulence of severe degree can be dangerous and there are forms that do demand the respect of the pilot. Flights near a cold front, near a thunderstorm, or un-

der heavy cumulus or cumulonimbus clouds may result in an unpleasant ride and some potential danger. In a sense, the turbulence is an early warning signal that the route of flight should be re-evaluated and weather information on the route ahead immediately updated.

A special form of turbulence is called "wake turbulence," and does have potential hazard. You may hear the pilot be warned by the phrase, "Caution, wake turbulence from departing 747." I remember my feeling of surprise when I heard a pilot warned, "Caution, wake turbulence from departing Aztec," as I lifted off of the runway. Even light twins can cause this phenomenon. All of this reflects the fact that the wing tips of large aircraft develop spinning vortices of wind that may endanger other aircraft in the immediate vicinity. These miniature but intense little whirlwinds are more marked near the site of takeoff or landing, so the region of the airport is the site of greatest risk. All that is necessary to avoid trouble is to wait until prevailing wind has blown these air disturbances away from the area—usually only a matter of two or three minutes, contingent on the direction and briskness of the wind. In calm air

Weather and Turbulence

in the vicinity of a large air terminal, a small plane flying overhead may feel sudden, sharp bumps many minutes after an airliner has passed overhead. These again are merely warnings of the intensity of this special kind of turbulence and will remind the pilot of the necessity of being aware of the safety of delaying take-off or landing behind a heavy aircraft.

Avoidance of all turbulence is an impossible dream, but its intensity and degree can be minimized by simple precautions. These are:

1. Fly early in the day when the weather is predicted to be hot. This seems like such an easy, sensible idea, but getting airborne always takes longer than you expect. Potential turbulence promotes alacrity.

2. Fly above cumulus cloud formations when possible as the air will be much smoother.

3. Give mountainous terrain either a wide berth or fly at a higher than usual altitude to avoid the swirling "mountain wave" that may occur.

4. Avoid the vicinity of thunderstorms and other chaotic weather. Squall lines are to be rigidly avoided!

5. Fly high on hot days.

6. Heed the advice of the tower with respect to wake turbulence and avoid the proximity of large aircraft during en route flight. It may be wise to request a delay in clearance for take-off or landing when a heavy jet has just used the runway.

Your pilot is trained to make certain adjustments in his technique of flight when updrafts and downdrafts make the ride unpleasant. He will slow the aircraft to below "maneuvering speed," change altitude, "attitude fly" using the artificial horizon to keep the plane straight and level rather than "chasing" the assigned altitude during a brief roller coaster ride. He may ask you to secure your seat belt, get a firm hold on something stable in the cabin and secure any loose objects that might be dislodged by the temporary jarring effect of a downdraft. If the teeth-jarring ride continues he may seek a higher altitude where things may settle down.

Any experienced flying companion will undergo turbulence and it can be safely prognosticated that she will never come to enjoy it. Only glider pilots who live for the convection currents that mean strong updrafts can be said to enjoy this form of thrill! Except for severe wake turbulence and entry into thunderstorms; neither of which a cautious pilot will allow you to experience, the usual forms of turbulence are more upsetting than hazardous. The aircraft designers have built more than enough resistance to the effects of such "G forces" for safe flight to continue.

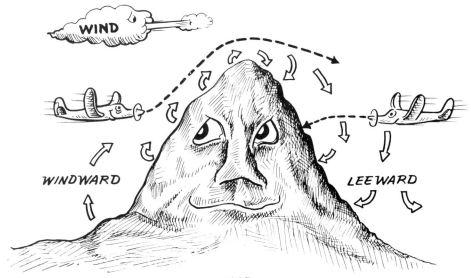

20

MEDICAL ASPECTS
OF FLYING

Have you ever experienced the sensation of safely arriving after a long flight in our "overcrowded airways," having seen only one or two other aircraft, and then been terrorized by an automobile trip on a truly crowded freeway to your home? There is some rationale for this sensation!

Thanks to Federal Air Regulations, rules for both the pilot's personal health and the mechanical health of aircraft are far more stringent than for the driving public. An airplane must be carefully maintained, with all repair work done by a certified mechanic. An annual inspection by experienced, licensed personnel is also mandatory. In short, there are no "jalopies of the air." Added to all of this is a system of required repairs which must be complete and certified within a specified period of time should some defect in a certain type of aircraft become apparent elsewhere in the country. The owner must comply with these "airworthiness directives;" a very different situation from the loose standards applied to the automobile-driving public.

In a sense, the same restrictions on aircraft health and maintenance are applied to the health and maintenance of the pilot. These restrictions are based on common sense, experience gained from the study of aircraft accidents, and the advice of experts in aviation medicine. They are formalized in Part 67 of the Federal Air Regulations; they are administered by the Federal Air Surgeon and his staff and implemented by a number of physicians designated as Aviation Medical Examiners. Although states vary in the rigidity of their laws concerning driver health—and no state is really very tough with respect to this—pilots must meet national standards by obtaining a medical examination which is quite exhaustive. This ensures the flying public that their pilot is physically able to operate the sophisticated aircraft of today. Since responsibilities of pilots differ—from the Sunday afternoon casual

Medical Aspects of Flying

"I'M GLAD I'M HERE WITH THE EAGLES INSTEAD OF DOWN THERE WITH THE CHICKENS!"

flyer who desires only the exhilaration of a short flight to enjoy the beauty of the skies and the feeling of being "an eagle up there, rather than a chicken down there"—to the vast complexity of a modern jet airliner and the lives of several hundred passengers dependent on his skill. Therefore, variations in the rigidity of physical standards are enforced. At the very minimum, the 747 pilot must have a complete examination at no greater than six month intervals. The degree of health he must maintain is much greater than the more casual pilot. The latter may need the less strict "third class medical" examination which is renewed each two years, but still makes a careful check of his general health.

In short, aircraft are kept in good health by Federal regulation and periodic inspection. Pilots must demonstrate good health when they begin their flying careers, and maintain acceptable health as certified by periodic examination.

Over the years, a number of accident prevention specialists and physicians have devoted their professional lives to aviation physiology and aviation safety. They have identified a series of potential problems with practical significance in relation to the health and safety of pilot and passengers. As a flying companion, you should be aware of these; since many of the problems involve decision-making by your pilot and your gentle input at times may help to preserve the highest levels of safety.

We can use the first six letters of the alphabet as a way of classifying and recalling the identified problems:

a. Altitude and Attitude: Altitude problems relate directly to the effects of oxygen "tension" in the blood. Each red blood cell has the potential of carrying a certain amount of oxygen to the "working tissues" of the body. This oxygen-carrying potential relates directly to the amount of red pigment (hemoglobin) in the red cell. This pigment is extremely efficient; if exposed to adequate supplies of oxygen it will quickly become saturated and ready for the task of supplying the body tissues. An intact system requires: adequate oxygen, adequate hemoglobin, a reasonably normal lung where the transfer of oxygen in the air to hemoglobin occurs, and an adequate set of blood vessels to function as a delivery system. For a healthy person, increasing altitude effects only the adequacy of the oxygen supply.

It is incorrect to think that the percentage of oxygen diminishes as one climbs. The major factor in reducing oxygenation of the blood is a decrease in the pressure of oxygen in higher atmospheres resulting in fewer molecules of oxygen uniting with hemoglobin. For convenience, we express the oxygen pressure in millimeters of mercury. At sea level this pressure is 159; at 20,000 feet it is 73! Depending on the rate of climb, the body can make adaptations to the reduced oxygen tension occurring during altitude gains of several thousand feet. Ultimately, however, these compensatory mechanisms fail and "hypoxia" (reduced oxygen tension in the body) occurs. The point at which hypoxia becomes a problem varies from individual to individual. One reads of World War I aces, in open cockpit planes without supplementary oxygen, lurking in the skies at 17,000 to 20,000 feet in order to pounce "out of the sun" on unsuspecting enemy planes at lower altitudes. These unique men had adaptive qualities the average mortal does not possess; we should heed the lessons modern aviation physiologists have taught us. Although altitude is a friend during emergencies when you need a long glide to find a suitable landing site; although altitude usually means smoother riding and reduced turbulence; although altitude may give a more beautiful panorama of the ground below—it may be a deadly enemy if you do not compensate for its effect by adequate oxygen.

Here are the basic rules to remember:

1. For most normal people supplementary oxygen is practical at 10,000 feet.

2. The Federal Air Regulations make supplementary oxygen mandatory at 12,500 feet.

3. For most normal people oxygen should be used above 5,000 feet during night flying.

4. Tobacco smokers, by virtue of a reduction in available hemoglobin molecules, should subtract 2,000 feet from each of the above values.

A word of explanation as to why hypoxia may be a problem. The retina of the eye is impaired and the pilot may not be as quick at seeing other aircraft. This effect is heightened at night as dark adaptation is selectively impaired. Brain function is altered. The decision-making processes are slowed. Rapid calculations become more difficult. Radio changes may be in error. Perhaps more important, however, is a peculiar sense of euphoria which can occur. Even while making important mistakes in judgement, the pilot feels clothed in invulnerability and does not see or admit his errors. A final problem, though rare, may be the most important of all.

Many "normal" people who function well at the altitude of their home and work, have difficulty after a rapid climb to high altitude because of early and unrecognized disease of arteries to the brain and heart wall. A combination of hypoxia and stress is particularly dangerous to such people.

As a flying companion, you can ensure the availability of oxygen when flights approach the levels discussed above. You can gently remind your pilot about the advantages of oxygen use when the altimeter creeps into the "danger" areas. None of this is necessary in the pressurized cabin found in some very sophisticated general aviation aircraft and the majority of commercial carriers, but the average pilot doesn't have the luxury of this kind of chariot. He should, therefore, have second best—adequate oxygen and the good sense to use it.

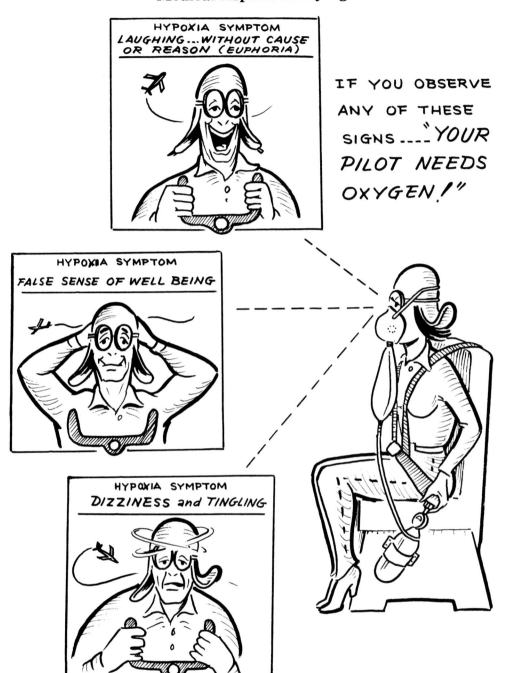

A handmaiden of altitude and hypoxia is known as hyperventilation. Under ordinary circumstances we all keep a nice balance between oxygen and carbon dioxide in our blood. If we exert ourselves physically, we need more oxygen and the working tissues produce more carbon dioxide. Our heart rate speeds to deliver the oxygen to the tissues and return carbon dioxide to the lung where it can be exhaled. We assist this by increasing the rate of breathing, and the balance is maintained. When confronted with stress or increased physical or mental work at high altitude, the very mechanisms that work so well on the ground become a potential source of danger. As we increase our rate of breathing we blow off too much carbon dioxide, and we are unconsciously "hyperventilating." When this occurs, a group of symptoms may appear and impair pilot efficiency. You can experience these by merely breathing very rapidly and deeply for three minutes. You will probably develop dizziness, numbness and tingling of the lips, hands and feet, and a loss of your sense of stability and well-being.

The combination of altitude and the oscillating motion of aircraft flight, coupled with the rapid head and eye movements as one scans the skies, notes the horizon, and checks the instrument panel, is conducive to vertigo. The problem may be intensified by passing in and out of clouds. It may be triggered by the effect of a rapidly blinking strobe light when flying at night, or through clouds or haze. Occasionally the stroboscopic effect of sunlight glinting off of the propeller of a single engine airplane flying toward the sun will cause severe vertigo.

As vertigo increases a sense of dizziness may give way to complete disorientation with respect to the position signals the pilot is receiving from his senses. If the flying companion is aware of an unusual aircraft position, such as a steepening descending turn, a comment may be enough to reinforce the pilot's need to refer solely to the flight instruments.

Unpleasant ear or sinus pain may occur as descent begins, since atmospheric pressure will increase. Pressure changes in the middle ear depend on an intact and open Eustachian tube. This same is true with sinuses, as the openings (ostia) to the nasal passages must be clear or pressure changes will be painful. Yawning, swallowing, or holding the nasal passages closed and increasing pressure by blowing gently with the mouth shut will usually alleviate the distress. Occasionally it is necessary to briefly gain altitude or make the descent in increments to avoid this unpleasant symptom.

Another condition coming logically under a discussion of altitude is acrophobia. This is an exaggerated and unreasonable fear of heights. Interestingly enough, the individual with acrophobia who becomes upset when looking out of a 10th story window, or who cannot stand to ride in an outside elevator, may be totally comfortable in an airplane cabin. Such individuals have difficulty arriving at a decision to make their first flight, but may be amazed to find that being in a cockpit at 5,000 feet is less distressing than looking over the edge of a 50 ft. cliff.

In summary, the answer to most altitude problems includes: good health, good flight planning, and the presence of supplementary oxygen for use when needed.

Attitude also enters into the safety of flight. We all have our "off" days. There are times when nothing seems to go right, or we are beset by family or business problems. This state of mind is not the proper psychological setting for operation of a sophisticated aircraft, and this is often more apparent to the flying companion than to the pilot. In this situation the flight probably should not be made and another form of transportation sought.

b. "Booze:" This inelegant term for alcoholic beverages allows us to continue with our alphabetical approach to medical hazards. This is a difficult problem; many aircraft accidents occur as a direct or indirect result of the use of alcohol!!!! The percentage of fatal accidents in this group is very high. The sad part of the whole subject is that alcoholic consumption is totally under the pilot's control. If he uses common sense and obeys the law, there will be no problem. If not, those who accompany him are seriously threatened. Here we again confront the problem of euphoria for the "glow" felt after consumption of alcohol impairs judgement. Alcohol actually reduces the ability of the brain to utilize oxygen, so that coordination, mood, and judgement are incrementally impaired by increasing altitude in the presence of alcohol in the bloodstream. In addition, alcohol clearly reduces dexterity and eye

efficiency, limits night sight, and may affect the inner ear causing earlier onset of vertigo.

Alcohol is absorbed rapidly into the system; it is slowly eliminated at a very consistent rate. Coffee, aspirin, cold showers, and other more esoteric devices for "sobering up" have no real effect on eliminating alcohol—popular notions to the contrary. The inebriated pilot may "feel better" after his tomato juice-Worcestershire sauce-raw egg concoction, but his performance as a pilot will not improve. Another misconception is that beer and wine are safe, because of their lower alcohol content, where "hard liquor" is not. This is simply not true! Rough equivalents are: 1 jigger of whiskey, gin, or vodka equals a pint of beer or five and one-half ounces of unfortified wine.

The law says, "eight hours from bottle to throttle." This should be considered an absolute minimum, particularly if a great deal of drinking was done. Of all areas discussed, it may well be here that the flying companion can exert the most forceful "voice of reason."

c. Carbon Monoxide: This gas is produced by fuel combustion and, contrary to expectations, is colorless, odorless, and tasteless. Fortunately, other products of combustion are easily detected; if exhaust odor is present one must assume the presence of carbon monoxide. Special color-changing carbon monoxide sensors can be purchased inexpensively, but with or without a sensor the basic rule is that the smell of exhaust should result in:

1. Turning off the heater, if it is operating.
2. Opening all outside air vents.
3. Landing at the first available airport.

d. Drugs and Disease: It is the duty of the Aviation Medical Examiner to issue or deny the appropriate medical certificate. In this handbook no comprehensive review of medical standards is needed. Suffice it to say that significant visual problems; ear, nose, and throat disorders; nervous diseases; cardiac problems; and diabetes mellitus all merit special attention. This reflects common sense. Good visual perception is a major defense against mid-air collision. Inner ear disorders may trigger disabling vertigo. Persons with convulsive disorders should not occupy the left seat of an aircraft. Altitude and periods of sudden stress may intensify many forms of heart disease. Persons with diabetes mellitus which necessitates medication for control should not become pilots. Wide swings in blood sugar or prolonged periods without appropriate food or medication could materially effect their safety and efficiency. Fortunately for the airman with milder forms of many disorders, there are appeal mechanisms to the Federal Air Surgeon so that each case can be decided on individual merit.

More important to both the pilot and his flying companion are the galaxy of "over the counter" medications that can affect pilot performance and flight safety. These medications break down handily into groups, but their effects are complex and highly variable from individual to individual. If in doubt about any personal medication used personally or by your pilot, advice should be obtained from a physician conversant with aircraft operation.

The groups include:
1. Anti-histamines
2. Tranquilizers
3. Anti-emetics, for control of nausea and vomiting.
4. Anti-diarrheal drugs
5. Some potent laxatives
6. Many appetite suppressants
7. Sedatives
8. Diuretics
9. Many drugs used for control of high blood pressure

Altitude, stress, and fatigue may intensify the action of any of these medicines. This should be considered by passengers, as well as the pilot. Particularly unpredictable are the actions of anti-histamine preparations so often contained in "cold remedies," and these should be avoided by all aboard.

Passengers who tend to be very tense at the prospect of flight and use tranquilizing medications in normal life should halve the dose if the flight may involve altitudes above 5,000 feet. Diuretics and laxatives should be avoided for obvious reasons of convenience; in addition, the majority of diuretics deplete the body stores of potassium, with the chance of unfavorable side-effects. Such medicines can be used at the completion of flight.

Diving presents special problems. It is popular in southern California to take SCUBA gear, fly to Baja California shores and spearfish or dive for langousta. A potentially dangerous medical problem may result. Diving, even to relatively shallow depths, increases the pressure ex-

erted by the watery atmosphere on the gases breathed. This is exactly the opposite situation as we have described in discussing hypoxia. During a dive, nitrogen is forced by pressure into body tissues, and after ascending from the dive the nitrogen is gradually released. If a dive is followed quickly by a flight to moderate altitude, the process is speeded; as the nitrogen bubbles expand in the body tissues, the diver-flyer becomes a victim of the "bends." Intense pain is felt throughout the muscles and it is urgent to immediately lose altitude and land as soon as possible. Unless the dive has been very deep or prolonged, the passage of two or three hours should alleviate danger of "bend" recurrence when flight is resumed.

e. Ego: The desire to master the complexities of the modern airplane demonstrates a significant amount of "ego strength." Casper Milquetoast or Walter Mitty may dream of skillfully piloting his cowering passengers through rain, hail, and fog to a perfect landing with a 100 foot ceiling and one-fourth mile visibility—all done on needle, ball, and airspeed and with one propeller feathered. The real pilot has gained confidence from study and practice and needs dream no such dreams to demonstrate his skill. In spite of this, there is an occasional situation which should be quickly perceived and adroitly handled by the intelligent flying companion. If the advice from the weather forecaster has been ominous; if the flight has been long and fatiguing; if the pilot admits to some indecision as to the wisdom of a difficult approach, or is clearly considering turning back for any good reason—this is the time the flying companion can state an opinion about wisdom vs. valor! Accident reports are replete with statements about "pilot error based on continued flight into adverse weather conditions." For everyone's safety—pilot, passengers, friends, and family; this is a time to be heard. A reassuring voice indicating that the braver decision may be to turn back, can avert disaster. The weight that tips the scales on the side of reason is often supplied by the intelligent, concerned, and knowledgeable passenger!

f. Fatigue: Only a moment need be spent on this aspect of the medical advice concerning aircraft operation. Fatigue does impair efficiency and a high level of competence is demanded in today's airways. Even "simple VFR flight" in bright, clear conditions can be hazardous when performed by a pilot who has pushed himself beyond his physiological limitations. By limiting pilot-in-command hours the airlines recognize this; so should the general aviation pilot. Air safety demands the highest level of efficiency and no emergency can be met by a tired, depleted airman. Here the flying companion can be of inestimable help by recognizing signs of fatigue and carefully making the necessary suggestions that will result in safe termination of the flight.

21

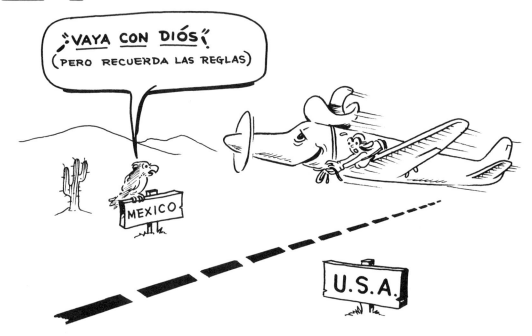

FLIGHT IN MEXICO

Any rules current today may be changed and it is important that no flight into Mexico be made without consultation with the F.A.A., discussion with Customs officials of the U.S. Customs Service, and also with pilot's organizations such as the A.O.P.A. Because of the unfortunate problems with illicit drugs crossing the Mexican-American border by aircraft, both Mexico and the United States have caused laws to be stringently enforced. This does not mean that flight into Mexico should be avoided. It does mean that the laws of both nations be respected!!!

Some of the most beautiful settings imaginable await the visitor coming by private airplane. Hundreds of border crossings are made daily. On any busy week-end you may have a wait of several minutes at Calexico or San Diego for Customs clearance due to the heavy traffic. The authors have made dozens of flights into Baja California as well as extensive flights into the "mainland" of Mexico. These have extended as far as Merida and Chichen Itza in the Yucatan peninsula; Mardi Gras at Verz Cruz (wild and wonderful); visits to the lovely Balboa Club and other resorts at Mazatlan, and a brief vacation by air to Puerta Vallarta.

Common to both central Mexico and Baja California are the general rules for flying in any part of Mexico. In summary, these include:

1. Proper identification of the ownership of the aircraft.

2. Tourist permits—obtained at any Mexican Consulate, or at the Mexican Port of Entry. A birth certificate, Voter's registration, or American passport will be needed to obtain this permit. It will be surrendered as you leave Mexico on the return home.

3. Proof by inspection that no firearms or other contraband are being brought into Mexico.

4. Filing of a Flight Plan and completion of a General Declaration Form. In

Flight in Mexico

order to complete these requirements at the Mexican Port of Entry it will be necessary to visit three offices: one for filing a Flight Plan; the Customs office (Aduana) where the inspector will make a search of your aircraft; and the Airport Commandante.

The American visitor will find the Mexican officials consistently courteous although the speed of activity may seem slow as compared with U.S. standards. Remember that this is, after all, a vacation in mananaland and begin your relaxation at the Border. It is proper and customary to leave a small tip for each official who handles your papers, and for the man or boy who escorts you from office to office.

The Mexican air route system has been modernized to an incredible degree in the past decade. The system of VOR's is present over much of Mexico and maps have improved markedly. Except in villages and small towns, runways are paved, well-maintained, long and wide. Nearly every village has an airport of some type as do the majority of the favorite hunting and fishing sites. The latter may be somewhat crude and the "high look" and "low look" advocated by Senterfitt in his *Airports of Baja California* is strongly advised at any uncontrolled airport. Repair facilities remain under-developed except at major cities, and long delays can be expected should mechanical difficulties occur. This must be accepted as one of the gambles you take to see new and interesting places.

Shopping in Mexico is a delight! Hand-crafted articles are for sale in almost every village. Items of dress such as rebozas, embroidered dresses from Yucatan, beach hats, sandals, bags, interesting tile and pottery, and baskets woven in hundreds of ways will be treasured remembrances of a trip "South of the Border."

Fishing and hunting are the targets for most men flying light aircraft into much of Mexico. The opportunities are incredible, even though the pressure of tourism has increased exponentially in the past few years. With even limited skill, the fisherman can have more action in Baja waters in a fortnight than he can in a year of angling along the California coast. Marlin, sailfish, dorado (mahi mahi), wahoo, roosterfish, totuava, and yellowtail are the major attractions, but smaller fish can be taken on light tackle to the

From White Knuckles to Cockpit Cool

angler's total edification. How long this happy situation will last is of concern to the Mexican government and to all sportsmen. The "long liners" of other foreign nations .can be seen on the horizon, harvesting huge quantities of fish and we can expect vigorous action by Mexico in the near future. Hunting is similarly excellent, particularly for dove, ducks, geese, and quail. A Mexican hunting license must be obtained, but in the event the hunter desires to bring a gun into Mexico, he must first visit the Mexican Consul's office with four 2" x 2" photographs, a letter from the sheriff or chief of police testifying to freedom from a criminal record, the registration number of his gun, and pay a fee. Hunting for wild game such as deer, jaguar, and javelina necessitates complex arrangements as large caliber rifles are not allowed to cross the border. Upland game shooting is coming under increased control, but the opportunities for success exceed the wildest dreams of most American hunters.

Sight-seeing pleasures are also incredible. The ruins at Chichen Itza, Palenque, and Uxmaul are "wonders of the world." Small cities such as Zihuatenejo and the nearly abandoned "Silver City" of Alamos are within easy access to the light airplane. Although a huge metropolis, Mexico City offers sights in the suburbs, at the Zocalo, and at the lovely park at Chapultepec that should not be missed. The same is true in the southern cities of Puebla, Oaxaca, and Tehuantepec. The market at Oaxaca is delightful and this city is close to the fascinating ruins of Mitla. Lovely hotels are available all over Mexico; even at some of the more "crude" fishing camps. This is particularly true at Merida and Cozumel in Yucatan, and at the tip of Baja California. At these places accommodations are truly luxurious and a "fishing widow" has no complaint. She can sip a Margarita under tropical skies, while sitting beside a large swimming pool scanning a varied menu. Mariachis or guitars complete the scene, and she may be heard to murmur: "Viva Mexico." "Viva Piper, Beechcraft, Cessna, and all the others."

FLIGHT INTO CANADA

Pleasure flight into Canada offers many of the same opportunities presented by flight into Mexico. It is hard to imagine anything more beautiful than Lake Louise, or the Banff and Jasper area. Shopping in Montreal, Toronto, or Vancouver offers a wide spectrum of delights, and the cuisine of Montreal and Quebec City matches any in the world. The Calgary Stampede is justifiably renowned, and the stately government buildings of Ottawa invite the expenditure of photography film. The Alcan Highway can be flown as a distant thread under the wings on the way to the excitement of Alaska. Just the opportunity to fly over the beautiful expanses of forests, lakes, the vast plains, as well as seeing the obvious productivity of this marvelous country is impressive. Although it necessitates a car rental, the trip to Toronto to see both the Guild Inn and drive to Stratford to view the outstanding Shakespeare almost makes the expense of a private airplane worth it!

Please realize that all of the above is presented without one word about hunting of the abundant game, or the pleasures of fishing! If you aren't convinced, your pilot will be when he contemplates the opportunity offered to the Nimrod or Isaak Walton that probably rests deeply in his soul.

Perhaps a compromise can be reached. You can visit some of the "watering places" such as Quebec City, Montreal, Toronto, Stratford, and Victoria; and he can have a week in the field stalking the wild goose. With an airplane this magic carpet journey is feasible. We have done it all; safely, reasonably inexpensively, and with the kind of memories that make reflection for this book a joy.

Flight in Canada and Mexico present many similarities, but they are far outweighed by the differences; and the flying companion takes a much more active part in Canadian flight planning. Although emerging rapidly, Mexico is an underdeveloped country with respect to general

127

aviation and many compromises are necessary. These have been alluded to in the previous chapter. Hard and fast rules are fewer for the pilot in Mexico and although the language may be something of a barrier, in general the attitude is relaxed and somewhat unstructured. Not so in Canada! Although there are only about 18,000 aircraft and 44,000 licensed pilots the tremendous distances, great variety of terrain, the explosive expansion of the northern portion of the country, the political aspects of two ethnic heritages, the military development, and the sophistication of the average Canadian citizen makes for a highly developed set of aircraft rules and regulations.

Flight planning in Canada is no paella. It is a carefully ordered series of courses which, if followed rigidly, will result in a sumptuous repast.

Consider for a moment some of the special problems with which the Ministry of Transport has had to contend. A small number include: huge numbers of migratory waterfowl, rocket launches from test sites, the military operations near the DEW line, the firing of Howitzers in winter to precipitate snow slides before they become dangerous, mortar calibration and proving ranges, areas of compass unreliability because of the proximity of part of the country to magnetic North, thousands of lakes, mountainous terrain, parachute jumping areas, mine blasting from open pit mines, dramatic temperature changes, and parts of the country where French is the predominant language.

General aviation has been a little slow to develop in Canada but not necessarily for the above reasons. Many of them stimulate private flying. The main problem has been the specter of taxes. When your pilot complains about the cost of his bird, or when you contemplate the budget changes it engenders; think of the Canadian. When he purchases an aircraft for personal use he pays a 12% general sales tax, up to an 8% tax levied by his Province, and a new 10% excise tax specifically directed at general aviation. In addition there is a 7½% tariff on imported aircraft which is fortunately not now being collected, but is "on the books." A user tax is in the offing with the suggestion being that there be a $5.00 assessment for each landing at any airport that has any kind of Federal support, or a flat $100.00/year levy. Now the Canadian pilot is also caught in an unfortunate political squeeze by what is known as Project BILCOM; a new law that requires the language at five Quebec airports used by the controllers to be French. Although not insurmountable, this imposes an additional load on the private pilot if he is not bilingual. Can't you hear your pilot trippingly enunciating "volets hyper-sustantateurs" when he means "flaps down"?

Fortunately these are Canadian problems and affect American pilots only indirectly. In spite of them, flight in Canada is not difficult and gives the flying companion her chance to excel. When the flight is being considered, she can write immediately for the necessary maps and information. Maps can be obtained by writing to:

Map Distribution Office
Department of Energy, Mines, and
 Resources
615 Booth Street
Ottawa 4, Canada

It is suggested that the initial letter describe the planned routes and request appropriate World Aeronautical Chart (WAC) Series, Canadian Pilotage Series, and Aeronautical Route Chart Series for VFR flight. It is also suggested that En Route Low Altitude Radio Navigation Charts and Terminal Area Charts be ordered even if IFR flight is not contemplated. Two books from the same office can be ordered, and this is suggested. They are **Canada Air Pilot (Pilots Handbook)** and **Canadian Aerodrome Directory.** To complete the package write for **Air Tourist Information** to:

Civil Aviation Branch
Department of Transport
Publications Branch
Queen's Printer
Ottawa 4, Canada

Most of these publications cost a small amount and you may be asked to remit a "cheque" before they are sent. One final pamphlet may be valuable to obtain. It is called **Weather Services are Free**, and is obtained by writing:

The Director, Meteorological Branch
Department of Transport
315 Bloor St., West
Toronto 5, Ontario, Canada

Armed with this material the flight planning can go on in earnest.

The following are a series of statements you should review with your pilot, and have stored in your memory when you fly in Canada.

1. Always file a Flight Plan or Flight Notification.

2. Always follow a Flight Plan or Flight Notification.

3. Always close a Flight Plan within 30 minutes of landing, and a Flight Notification in less than 24 hours after landing.

4. Carry the designated Emergency Equipment if flying in a Sparsely Settled Area (See Appendix).

5. If you make a forced landing, stay by your aircraft.

6. Build and maintain a smoke fire as soon as possible after a forced landing.

7. VFR "on top" is illegal in Canada.

8. VFR at night or from a military aerodrome require a Flight Plan.

9. When IFR or flying under "controlled VFR" conditions, position reports will be necessary unless specifically released because of radar coverage.

10. Above 3500 feet over terrain, flight should be on odd thousands (1000, 3000, 5000, etc.) from 000 to 179 degrees, and on even thousands from 180 to 359 degrees.

11. When flying in uncontrolled airspace continuously monitor 122.2 MHz, and give frequent position reports as well as declaring your intention to change altitude.

12. Remember that Canada requires notification prior to entry into the country. A Flight Plan filed on contact with an American Flight Service Station designating a Canadian destination suf-

fices if a specific request is made to notify Canadian Customs and Immigration Service.

13. Expect to pay a special charge if the Customs official has to come to the port of entry at other than usual working hours.

14. On entry be prepared to show a valid pilot's license, Aircraft Log Book, and unrestricted Certificate of Airworthiness.

15. If multiple stops are planned in Canada request from the Customs official a "Cruising Permit" which will be good for three months and obviates the necessity of landing at a port of entry when leaving Canada so long as goods are not carried that require documentary control.

16. Remember that an Emergency Locator Transmitter is a mandatory piece of equipment when flying in Canada.

17. Be familiar in advance with the Terminal Radar Service Areas (TRSA) at large metropolitan centers, which largely coincide with the Terminal Control Areas (TCA) of the United States. Canadian TRSA's do not require transponder or encoding altimeter at the time of this writing.

18. If initial entry into Canada is to be at a smaller Aerodrome of Entry and Exit, it is best to write, call, or telegraph your intentions, requesting a reply in writing. This will establish "your bona fides" if you should land at the wrong airport by error.

19. Be familiar with the area called Block Airspace as flight is forbidden unless your pilot is instrument rated and has properly filed.

20. Be familiar with the "standard pressure region" which makes up a large part of Canada, and where the altimeter should be set to 29.92 inches once altitude has been reached.

21. Remember that a one hour notification to Customs officials of the United States is necessary prior to re-entry. This is true for the majority of both "international airports" as defined by the Secretary of the Treasury or Commissioner of Customs, or "landing rights airports" where the right to land is under the control of a Customs official with concurrence of Immigration and Naturalization Service, the Public Health Service, and the Animal and Plant Health Inspection Service of the Department of Agriculture. If in doubt about the one hour advance notice make a prior check to avoid difficulty.

22. As with Mexico, United States officials require: type of aircraft, aircraft registration number, name of pilot-in-command, point of last departure, airport of arrival, number and citizenship of passengers, and estimated time of arrival at the U.S. port of entry.

As with Mexico, a good guest obeys the laws of the country she visits, and courteous behavior is nearly always repaid in kind.

ISLAND ADVENTURE

When the western flyer is first confronted with island flying in the Florida keys and the Bahamas, the reaction may be one of amazement at the low altitudes normally flown. Except for the Gold Coast along the highly developed beach areas and an occasional television tower, hazards to aerial navigation such as mountain waves, icing conditions, precipitous terrain, and strong up and downdrafts are only a memory. Planning is directed at the problems of flying over swampy ground, open water, and the unique weather characteristics of Florida, the keys, and the Bahamas. These include sudden squalls arising out over the ocean, the hurricane season with its threat to the non-hangared aircraft, periods of fog and low ceilings, and embedded thunderstorms. Fortunately the U.S. Weather Service has excellent storm tracking facilities, and heavy precipitation and thunderstorms are "painted" on the radar screen, thereby offering adequate advance warning. It is also a happy circumstance that weather in the islands and south Florida is excellent during the majority of the year, and VFR flying is the rule rather than the exception.

Key West is a fascinating objective. Here is the southernmost city in the United States, with a tropical feeling unknown elsewhere in our country. Here also is a complete little city with a dramatic history and all of the amenities a vacationer could desire. In either the past or present the southern keys have figured prominently in the shrimp industry, cigar making, rum running, buccaneering, salvaging of wrecked ships from the reefs, turtle capture, fishing, scuba diving, Naval history, and literature. Ernest Hemingway, Tennessee Williams, John Dewey, Robert Frost, and Harry Truman are names associated with Key West, and the city does an excellent job in presenting their stories. While the pilot amuses himself with a fishing trip out off of the reef, the flying companion can visit the excellent museum at East

From White Knuckles to Cockpit Cool

Martello Tower, Hemingway's home, or the many old houses demonstrating what is designated as "conch architecture." Such culinary delights as conch chowder, Cuban sandwiches, and key lime pie are unique to the lower keys and satisfying to the palate. No visitor should miss the Conch Tour Train which presents a comprehensive guide to the city. The fashion conscious woman must plan a stop at Mallory Square where silk screening of fabrics is still laboriously done by hand in a factory open to visitors. It will take a strong will, or a heavily packed airplane, to resist the temptation of purchasing material for a new outfit!

The flight down the keys is safe and the varied colors of the sea delight the eye. Taking off from one of the major airports of south Florida, the pilot has a series of excellent airfields along his route, as well as Highway 1 connecting the string of little islands with a series of bridges, including one seven miles in length. Stops at Ocean Reef and Marathon can be made by the couple enjoying a leisurely trip and both resorts have excellent airports. These are busy fields as the "snowbirds" from the north have learned of the advantages of south Florida and the keys, and they migrate in large numbers when the weather deteriorates at home.

The venturesome couple can continue beyond Key West by air to circle the remains of Fort Jefferson on the Dry Tortugas. This is the site of the imprisonment of Dr. Samuel Mudd in 1869 after his conviction of complicity in the assasination of President Lincoln. Float plane trips can be arranged for those wishing to tramp through the old fort.

The west coast of Florida also gives an opportunity for island flying and stops along the rapidly developing Gulf shore. Marco Island is a tremendous recreational and "second home" development with an airport, hotels, car rental, fine restaurants, and all of the other facilities a vacationer could desire. Shelling along the miles of white sand beaches compete with the Great Barrier Reef, and fishing is also notable.

Island flying in the far west is limited to flights to Catalina Island off the southern California coast. The airport is situated on the top of a mountain rising steeply from the surf. The usual landing involves an approach toward the bluff from the east because of the prevailing westerly breeze, and it can be an exciting moment as the pilot touches down a few hundred feet from the sheer drop. Catalina Airport is famous for its luncheons—hamburgers and steaks eaten on a terrace looking toward the sea and the southern part of the island. Tours into Avalon are available and during the drive into the village you anticipate seeing bison and cattle placidly grazing in the meadows. Avalon is a haven for hundreds of yachts during the summer season and the flight from Long Beach or Los Angeles will pass numbers of small boats heading toward Avalon harbor. This was Zane Grey's home for years, and the island is still famous for deep sea fishing and big game hunting.

There is limited island flying in the northwest in the San Juan Islands, but this is predominantly boating territory at present. As the San Juans continue their rapid development more facilites for the airman can be anticipated.

The Bahamas add the thrill—and the complications—of leaving the territory of the United States and entering a foreign country. There are some seven hundred islands in the Bahamas chain, and a moderate climate prevails, influenced by the gulf stream. An ambitious program of tourism encourages the American pilot to visit this new nation and the entire economy is tourist-oriented. Nassau and Freeport are the usual ports of entry although other airports are also designated. First touchdown must be at a port of entry where Customs and Immigration will clear the aircraft and passengers. Necessary documents include a "Special Declaration for Private Aircraft"

Island Adventure

prepared in triplicate, as well as the completion of immigration cards for each occupant of the aircraft. The "Special Declaration" can be obtained and filled out prior to leaving the United States. Most airports serving the general area of eastern Florida have these available. One copy of this form should be retained on board and used as a "cruising permit" while traveling in the Bahamas. The immigration cards are completed on arrival at the port of entry. Although the rigidity of the rule may vary, the Bahamas Tourist Bureau will indicate that to legally receive an immigration card, proof of identity as furnished by an American passport, birth certificate, or voter's registration is necessary. To avoid delay, one of these should be taken on the flight and be presented to the Bahamian official on arrival. No special inoculations are required although on your return to the U.S. you will be required to clear through the office of the U.S. Public Health Service.

So long as your aircraft remains above 25 degrees north latitude and your cruising speed is less than 180 knots a routine flight plan is all that is needed to comply with American regulations. Your pilot will cross the Air Defense Identification Zone (ADIZ) marked on your maps, but in the circumstances of the usual flight the only addition to his VFR flight plan is a notification of the time he will cross an ADIZ boundary.

There are more than fifty airstrips in the Bahamas, varying from giant airports with runways capable of handling anything less than the Concorde—and maybe even that—to short, rough strips with questionable maintenance. Local enquiry is obviously necessary before tackling anything such as the latter. Since tiedown facilities at small airports may be absent chocks, stakes, and ropes are suggested.

Your pilot will need to provide life jackets for each passenger and the plane should have full tanks at each stop. Gasoline of 100 octane rating is generally available although as the distance from major airports increases, the cost will rise significantly. Weather information is obtainable from either U.S. or Bahamian radio stations. Navigation aids are excellent, with both VOR's and low frequency beacons scattered throughout the island chain.

Every level of accommodation is available. During the "season," which usually extends from December 15 to April 20, prices are substantially higher than the remainder of the year and it is wise to have reservations made and confirmed before leaving the United States. In the "Out Islands" one can anticipate lower prices and more relaxed atmosphere. In these remote locales the main attractions are the "wind, sand and stars," and you will be very much on your own.

Island flying necessitates no unusual piloting skills—just good planning, sound maintenance, full tanks, and life jackets aboard!

Runways in lightly inhabited areas may have rather barren facilities; often innocent of windsocks or other navigation aids. Landing without information about the wind, and particularly if the choice were toward the sea, could end up in a dunking. At Hana, Maui where this runway is, the help of blowing smoke or dust would assist in a decision as to landing direction.

A
Glossary Of Terms, Contractions, and Acronyms

ACROPHOBIA: Abnormal fear of height.

ACTIVE RUNWAY: Runway in use for takeoff or landing.

ADF: Automatic direction finder. A low frequency navigation instrument used for "homing" to a station.

AGL: Above ground level.

AILERON: A hinged control surface on the wing which enables the plane to roll or bank.

AIRMET: Meteorological advisory of significance to light aircraft.

AIRWAYS: "Highways in the sky" which represent designated routes; numbered on charts.

ALTIMETER: An aneroid barometer which indicates altitude above sea level instead of atmospheric pressure.

ANNUAL: Airframe and engine inspection required each 12 months.

AOPA: Aircraft Owners and Pilots Association.

APPROACH PLATES: Small sheets showing specific procedures for instrument landing at an airport with instrument capability. An airport map.

ASR: Airport surveillance radar.

ATIS: Automatic terminal information service—an airport informational frequency.

ATR: Airline transport rating.

AZIMUTH: An arc of the horizon measured clockwise 360 degrees from true north—often used synonymously with "compass rose."

BASE LEG: The crosswind component of the landing pattern.

BENDS: A painful and potentially dangerous illness caused by the release of nitrogen from tissues. It may be precipitated by SCUBA diving followed by flight.

BURBLE: Shaking or quivering of the plane at slow speeds when approaching a stall.

CARBURETOR HEAT: Device to pre-heat air entering the carburetor to prevent ice formation or melt accumulated ice.

CAVU: Clear and visibility unlimited.

CEILING (AIRCRAFT): The maximum altitude the plane is capable of attaining under standard conditions.

CEILING (METEOROLOGY): The height of the base of a cloud formation when the degree is classified as broken, overcast, or obscured and not classified as "thin" or "partial."

CHECK LIST: A written list of necessary tasks before each takeoff and landing.

CHECK POINT: A visual or electronic landmark used to establish the position of the aircraft.

COMPASS (GYRO): A gyroscopic, relatively stable instrument to identify direction; calibrated by reference to the wet compass.

COMPASS (WET): A directional instrument using the pull of magnetic north for calibration; a small, floating magnet suspended in fluid.

COMPASS ROSE: Various diagramatic representations of the points of the compass; some ornate, and some merely a circle marked with the principal points of the compass.

CONTROL ZONE: The area about one or more airports, usually with a five mile radius and extensions for arrival or departure paths, extending upward from the surface of the ground.

CONVECTION: Vertical air movements such as occur from heated surfaces.

COURSE: Direction to destination measured on a chart.

CROSS WIND: Wind blowing from the right or left of the aircraft heading.

CUMULONIMBUS: A "thunderhead" cloud formed by rising currents of air. The "anvil cloud" is a cumulus or cumulonimbus cloud with an anvil configuration in the upper portion denoting high wind velocity.

DENSITY ALTITUDE: A calculation of theoretical density of a standardized atmosphere at a given altitude. This altitude has more significance relative to aircraft performance than the actual altitude.

DEW POINT: The temperature at which vapor begins to condense.

DME: Distance measuring equipment measuring nautical miles to a navigation facility with Tacan capability.

ELEVATOR: Movable part of the horizontal tail surface, concerned with lateral axis, or pitch.

ELT: Emergency locator transmitter.

EMERGENCY RADIO FREQUENCY: 121.5 mHz.

EMERGENCY TRANSPONDER CODE: 7700.

ENVELOPE: The calculated limits of safety in airplane loading affected by weight and change in center of gravity.

ETA: Estimated time of arrival.

FAA: Federal Aviation Administration.

FBO: Fixed Base Operator.

FEATHERED PROPELLER: Propeller blades rotated to result in the minimum wind resistance.

FIREWALL: Division between the engine compartment and the cabin.

FIX: An accurate geographical position of the airplane, or a navigation point on the ground.

FLAPS: Sections of the trailing edge of the wing that can be lowered and raised, functioning as "air brakes" and to increase lift.

FLIGHT PLAN: A formalized plan of flight filed with a Flight Service Station.

FLIGHTWATCH: 122.0 mHz—a radio frequency for detailed weather information.

FRONT: Zone between two masses of air having different density and temperature.

FSS: Flight Service Station.

FUEL SUMP: Dependent portion of fuel system where water or sediment may accumulate.

G FORCE: Gravity.

GEAR: Aircraft wheel system.

GLIDE SLOPE: Part of the instrument landing system relating to altitude on final approach.

GROUND CONTROL: The radio frequency from which instructions are received for any aircraft movement on the ground prior to entry onto a runway.

GROUND LOOP: An uncontrollable violent turn of the aircraft on the ground.

GROSS WEIGHT: The maximum weight to which the aircraft can be safely loaded.

GUMP: The standardized quick checklist prior to landing, including: Gas, Undercarriage, Mixture, Propeller.

GYRO INSTRUMENTS: Directional gyro, artificial horizon, and some turn indicators.

HEADING: Direction the nose of the airplane points during flight.

HIGH: An area of high atmospheric pressure with a closed circulation.

HIGH LOOK: Observation of a runway from high altitude.

HOMING: Flying directly toward a radio beacon.

HYPOXIA: Reduced oxygen tension in the body.

IFR: Flying according to instrument flight rules.

ILS: Instrument landing system.

INVERSION: Weather term indicating a layer of air in which temperature rises with increased altitude.

KPH: Kilometers-per-hour — not knots-per-hour.

LENTICULAR CLOUD: Lens-shaped cloud, usually associated with high wind velocity.

LOG BOOK: The written record of all flights,

kept by the pilot.

LOW: An area of low atmospheric pressure; a depression.

LOW LOOK: Low altitude flight over a runway to view landing conditions.

MAGNETO: Part of an aircraft ignition system creating the spark to ignite the fuel/air mixture.

MAYDAY: An international vocal distress signal.

MEA: Minimum en route altitude.

MILLIBAR: A unit of atmospheric pressure. When divided by 33.9, the result will be expressed in inches of mercury.

MISSED APPROACH: A prescribed route of flight when a landing under instrument conditions cannot be successfully completed.

MPH: Statute miles-per-hour.

MSL: Mean sea level.

NDB: Non-directional beacon, used in navigation.

NINETY-NINES: An incorporated organization of women pilots primarily concerned with aviation safety and education.

NOTAM: Notices to Airmen, usually relating to changing conditions at airports, air routes, and weather advisories.

OCCLUDED FRONT: Front created by a cold front overtaking a warm or stationary front.

OCTANE: A gasoline rating system. Light aircraft usually use 80 octane gasoline which is red, 100 octane gasoline which is green, or new low-lead which is blue.

OIL: Lubricating fluid used in aircraft engines. Both detergent and non-detergent forms are used.

OMNI: A very high frequency navigation aid transmitting from 108 to 118 mHz and used synonymously with VOR (Very High Frequency Omni Range).

ON THE NUMBERS: A slang usage to indicate touchdown with the wheels at the very threshold where the numbers are normally painted.

PAR: Precision approach radar; an extremely accurate device used in landing under instrument conditions.

PATTERN: Route flown at landing, normally consisting of a 45 degree entry, 180 degree downwind leg, 90 degree base leg, and 0 degree final leg.

PATTERN ALTITUDE: Prescribed altitude when flying the landing pattern. Traditionally, this has been 800 feet above ground level.

PILOTAGE: Flight in VFR conditions by reference to visible landmarks on the terrain.

PIREP: Pilot report of sky, wind, and weather conditions.

PITOT-STATIC SYSTEM: An open system controlling the function of the altimeter, air speed indicator, and vertical speed indicator, using the ram effect of air.

PRECESSION: The slow gyration of the rotation axis of a spinning body reflecting a torque effect.

PSI: Pounds per square inch.

RADIAL: Course projected by a VHF radio range; a magnetic bearing from a VOR.

RIME ICE: Irregular, granular icing created by freezing of water droplets at or near freezing.

RON: Remain overnight.

RPM: Revolutions per minute.

RVR: Runway visual range.

RUDDER: The movable part of the vertical tail surface concerned with movement of the airplane about a vertical axis (yaw).

SECTIONAL CHARTS: Navigational charts detailing landmarks and terrain used in pilotage.

SEQUENCE REPORTS: An abbreviated, hourly updated report of weather, sky, and wind conditions at a specific weather station.

SIGMET: Meteorological advisory of importance to all aircraft.

SHORT FIELD: A runway of limited length necessitating adjustments in takeoff or landing technique.

SIMPLEX: Radio frequency for both sending and receiving voice transmissions.

SOFT FIELD: Runway consistency necessitating adjustments in technique of takeoff or landing.

SQUALL LINE: A narrow line of active thunderstorms; usually preceding a rapidly moving cold front and associated with highly turbulent weather.

STABILIZER: The fixed part of the horizontal tail surface.

STOL: Short takeoff and landing; usually referring to modifications of an aircraft or a special model having these characteristics.

SUMPS: The dependent portion of the fuel system; used for drainage of foreign material from fuel.

TCA: Terminal control area.

THRESHOLD: The area adjacent to the

beginning of the runway.

THUNDERSTORM: An intense weather disturbance with strong gusts, rain, hail, thunder and lightning, created in a cumulonimbus cloud.

TOWER SETTING: The radio frequency for transmitting and receiving transmissions from an airport control tower.

TRANSPONDER: A radar transmitter "painting" an image on a radar screen on the ground; used in aircraft identification and traffic separation.

TRSA: Terminal radar service area.

TURBO: A form of "supercharger" using waste engine gases to improve aircraft performance at high altitude.

TWERP: The flying companion checklist including **Traffic**, **Windsock**, **Elevation** of the airport, **Radios**, **Pumps**.

UHF: Ultra-high frequency.

UNICOM: The radio frequencies used for airport advisory service or pilot convenience requests — 122.8 mHz at airports without a control tower, and 123.0 at airports with a control tower.

USEFUL LOAD: The "payload" of an aircraft including fuel, oil, passengers, pilot, and baggage.

VECTOR: Heading issued to the pilot in radar navigation.

VERTIGO: Dizziness and malaise which may result in spatial disorientation.

VFR: Visual Flight rules.

VHF: Very high frequency.

VOR: An acronym for **Very** high frequency **Omni** **Range** and generally used synonymously for the station sending the signal and the receiver in aircraft. *radio freq.*

VORTAC: As above, but with the addition of ultra high frequency Tacan capability.

WAC: World Aeronautical Chart.

WAKE TURBULENCE: A potentially dangerous air disturbance caused by wingtip vortices created by large aircraft.

WARM FRONT: An air disturbance at the junction of an advancing body of warm air and a retreating body of colder air.

WINDSOCK: A cloth or plastic sleeve mounted aloft at an airport for use in estimating wind direction and velocity.

WINDTEE: A "T" shaped device, often resembling a miniature airplane freely rotating in the wind to indicate landing or takeoff direction.

WINDS ALOFT: A description of the winds at varying altitudes above ground giving direction and velocity, and characteristically at 3000 foot increments.

YOKE: The "wheel" used by the pilot to alter the position of the elevator and ailerons.

ZULU TIME: Greenwich mean time, used to standardize statements of time.

B
Line Boy Check List

1. Airplane wheels chocked . . . . ——
2. No smoking . . . . ——
3. Verify octane rating of gasoline—check filler cap lines to pump or truck, and color (80/87-red; 100/130-green;low lead-blue) . . . . ——
4. Check grounding of truck to aircraft . . . . ——
5. Check gasoline level visually in all tanks . . . . ——
6. Check seating of gasoline caps . . . . ——
7. Drain sumps for evidence of water or sediment . . . . ——
8. Check oil level . . . . ——
9. Know proper oil level, oil weight, and whether detergent or non-detergent . . . . ——
10. Check seating of oil dipstick . . . . ——
11. Supervise tiedown and secure ailerons and elevator . . . . ——
12. Securely lock door and baggage compartments if overnight stay . . . . ——

C

RON (Remain Overnight) Check List

1. Pack overnight kit prior to flight .... ——
2. .Have credit cards available .... ——
3. Check via AOPA's *Airports U.S.A.*, or other manual re
   motels offering transportation at destination .... ——
4. About 30 miles out, call Unicom (122.8 or 123.0) advising
   time of arrival, and requesting that reservation and transportation be arranged .... ——
5. Supervise line boy upon landing (See Line Boy Check List) . ——
6. Secure ailerons, elevator and cover instrument panel .... ——
7. Watch fueling and tiedown procedure .... ——
8. If early departure anticipated, pay fuel and tiedown charges ——
9. Check weather for 12 and 18 hour en route forecast .... ——
10. Remind pilot to close flight plan. .... ——

D

Survival Kit

1. Survival booklet, such as Boy Scout Handbook .... ——
2. Waterproof matches, or butane lighter .... ——
3. Water .... ——
4. Desert still, for water-making .... ——
5. Signal flares .... ——
6. Knife—such as Swiss Army knife .... ——
7. Signal panels .... ——
8. Signaling mirror .... ——
9. Candles and flashlight with spare batteries .... ——
10. Water purification tablets, such as Halazone .... ——
11. Heavy duty aluminum foil .... ——
12. Nylon cord .... ——
13. Fishing kit .... ——
14. Pliers—combination type .... ——
15. Nylon cloth canopy .... ——
16. Plastic bags .... ——
17. Compass .... ——
18. Wire—small roll .... ——
19. File—three corner .... ——
20. Food—hiker's dried food excellent .... ——
21. Hard candy, jerky, hard chocolate .... ——
22. Emergency Locator Beacon .... ——

E

Airplane "First Aid" Kit

1. Airplane *Owner's Handbook* .... —
2. Tie down ropes .... —
3. Tie down stakes .... —
4. Chocks for wheels .... —
5. Chamois .... —
6. Scale .... —
7. Windshield cleansing agent .... —
8. Paper towels .... —
9. Sick sacks .... —
10. Tool kit .... —
11. Flashlight, with spare batteries .... —
12. Portable oxygen if no oxygen system .... —
13. Extra door key .... —
14. Extra oil, if flight out of U.S. anticipated .... —

F

Density Altitude Table

Technique: Set altimeter to 29.92 to obtain pressure altitude. Read across from this value to the present temperature. The result will be the Density Altitude.

Pressure Altitude	*C-15 **F-59	C-20 F-68	C-25 F-77	C-30 F-86	C-35 F-95	C-40 F-104	C-45 F-113	C-50 F-122	Increase In Takeoff Run	Decrease In Rate Of Climb
Sea Level	0	550	1100	1650	2200	2750	3300	3850	0	0
1000 ft.	1200	1750	2300	2850	3400	3950	4500	5050	11%	10%
2000	2450	3000	3550	4100	4650	5200	5750	6300	23%	19%
3000	3650	4200	4750	5300	5850	6400	6950	7500	37%	28%
4000	4900	5450	6000	6550	7100	7650	8200	8750	52%	37%
5000	6100	6650	7200	7750	8300	8850	9400	9950	70%	45%
6000	7300	7850	8400	8950	9500	10050	10600	11150	91%	53%
7000	8550	9100	9650	10200	10750	11300	11850	12400	117%	60%
8000	9750	10300	10850	11400	11950	12500	13050	13600	145%	66%
9000	11000	11550	12100	12650	13200	13750	14300	14850	182%	72%
10000	12200	12750	13300	13850	14400	14950	15500	16050	235%	77%

* Celsius temperature
** Fahrenheit temperature

G
International Morse Code And Phonetic Alphabet

	MORSE CODE	PHONETIC ALPHABET
A	• —	Alpha
B	— • • •	Bravo
C	— • — •	Charley
D	— • •	Delta
E	•	Echo
F	• • — •	Foxtrot
G	— — •	Golf
H	• • • •	Hotel
I	• •	India
J	• — — —	Juliet
K	— • —	Kilo
L	• — • •	Lima
M	— —	Mike
N	— •	November
O	— — —	Oscar (pronounced Os-ka)
P	• — — •	Papa
Q	— — • —	Quebec (pronounced Kee-bek)
R	• — •	Romeo
S	• • •	Sierra
T	—	Tango
U	• • —	Uniform
V	• • • —	Victor
W	• — —	Whiskey
X	— • • —	X-Ray
Y	— • — —	Yankee
Z	— — • •	Zulu

H
Bahamian Nav-Com Frequencies

FLIGHT SERVICE STATIONS:

Miami 126.7
Grand Bahama United States
Air Force Base 126.9
Nassau, and remoted sites at Bimini,
Marsh Harbour, Governor's Harbour,
George Town 124.2
Freeport, Grand Bahama 122.3
Unicom—Out Island resorts 122.8

TOWERS:

Freeport 118.5
Nassau 119.5
West End 119.8

VOR:

Bimini 116.7
Freeport 113.2
Nassau 112.7

LOW FREQUENCY BEACONS:

Location	Code	Frequency
Andros Town	ZCB	203
Bimini	ZBV	396
Freeport	ZFP	209
George Town	ZGT	240
Governor's Harbour	ELJ	224
Grand Bahama AFB	GBN	326
Marsh Harbour	ZMH	203
Nassau	ZQA	251
Rock Sound	RSD	353
San Salvador	SSJ	281
Treasure Cay	ZTC	233
Walker's Cay	ZWC	263
West End	ZWE	317

WEATHER:

Freeport . . . . Telephone: 2-7944
Nassau . . . . Telephone: 7-7178

I
VORs In Mexico

ACA	Acapulco, Gro.	115.9	MXL	Mexicali, B.C.	115.0
CPE	Campeche, Cam.	112.8	MEX	Mexico, D.F.	117.0
CME	Ciudad Del Carmen, Cam.	113.0	MTY	Monterrey, N.L.	114.7
DEL	Ciudad Delicias, Chin.	113.5	NOG	Nogales, Son.	112.5
CJS	Ciudad Juarez, Chin.	116.7	OAX	Oaxaca, Oax.	112.0
CEN	Ciudad Obregon, Son.	115.1	QET	Queretaro, Oro.	115.7
CVM	Ciudad Victoria, Tam.	113.7	REX	Reymosa, Tam.	112.4
CTM	Chetumal, Q. Roo	112.4	SRL	Santa Rosalia, B.C.	112.6
CZM	Cozumel, Q. Roo	112.6	TAM	Tampico, Tam.	117.5
CUL	Culican,Sin.	112.1	TMN	Taumin, S.L.P.	113.3
DGO	Durango, Dgo.	112.2	TAP	Tapachula, Chis.	115.3
GDL	Guadalajara, Jal.	117.3	TEQ	Tequisquitengo, Gro.	113.1
HMO	Hermosillo, Son.	112.8	TIJ	Tijuana, B.C.	113.8
LAP	La Paz, B.C.	112.3	TRC	Torreon, Coah.	116.4
LMM	Los Mochis, Sin.	115.5	TGZ	Tuxtla Gutierrez, Chis.	113.9
MAT	Matamoros, Tam.	114.3	VER	Vera Cruz, Ver.	112.9
MID	Merida, Yuc.	117.7	VSA	Villahermosa, Tam.	117.3
MZT	Mazatlan, Sin.	114.9	NLD	Nuevo Laredo, Tam.	112.6

Furnished by the courtesy of Southwest Air
Rangers, El Paso, Texas

J
Mexico Check List

1. Aircraft ownership identification and air-worthiness certificate . . . . ——
2. Tourist permits . . . . ——
3. Emergency kit including Halazone tablets, desert still, matches, signal flares, fishing gear . . . . ——
4. First aid kit . . . . ——
5. Tie-down ropes . . . . ——
6. Chamois for fuel filtration . . . . ——
7. Maps of Mexico . . . . ——
8. Senterfitt's *Airports of Mexico* or *Airports of Baja California*, or the equivalent . . . . ——
9. Anti-diarrheal agent . . . . ——
10. Pesos, U.S. coins, and dollar bills for tipping . . . . ——
11. Large flashlight and extra batteries . . . . ——

PROCEDURAL CHECK LIST:
1. Notify family or friends of itinerary . . . . ——
2. File "round robin" flight plan with U.S. Flight Service Station . . . . ——
3. Land first at designated Mexican Port of Entry. Show proof of U.S. citizenship. . . . . ——
4. Complete Flight Plan, General Declaration Form, clear Customs and office of the Commandante . . . . ——

5. Follow the Flight Plan filed with Mexican authorities explicitly—no deviations!!!! .... ____

6. When leaving Mexico again land at a Port of Entry and surrender tourist permits and General Declaration Form ...... ____

7. When estimated time of arrival at a U.S. Port of Entry is firm, a call should be made 1 hour in advance of estimated arrival to a Flight Service Station asking that U.S. Customs be notified. Information needed:
   a. Type of aircraft
   b. Aircraft registration number
   c. Pilot's name
   d. Estimated time of arrival
   e. Where flight originated outside of U.S.
   f. Number and citizenship of passengers ____

8. On landing in the United States remain in the aircraft until the U.S. Customs official has cleared you to leave the plane. ____

K
Emergency Equipment Required For Flight Over A "Sparsely Settled Area" In Canada

1. For each person carried, five pounds of concentrated food or its equivalent that is of high nutritive value and not subject to damage by heat or cold and has been inspected by the owner of the aircraft or his representative not more than six months prior to flight, the food to be contained in a waterproof package bearing a tag or label upon which is certification of such inspection
2. Adequate cooking utensils and mess tins
3. Matches in a waterproof container
4. Portable compass
5. An axe of two and one-half pounds or heavier with a twenty-eight inch handle
6. Thirty feet of snare wire
7. A sharp jack-knife or hunting knife of good quality
8. Additional equipment during summer conditions consisting of: four trawls, two fishing lines with an assortment of hooks and sinkers and a fish net of not more than two inch mesh, sufficient mosquito nets to accommodate all persons carried
9. Additional equipment during winter conditions consisting of: sufficient tents to accommodate all persons carried or, in lieu thereof, engine or wing covers of suitable design and material, sufficient sleeping bags to accommodate all persons carried, and two pairs of snowshoes

ADDITIONAL EMERGENCY EQUIPMENT SUGGESTED:
1. Spare axe handle
2. Honing stone or file
3. Ice chisel
4. Snow knife
5. Snow shovel
6. Flashlight with spare bulbs and batteries
7. Pack sack
8. Insect repellent
9. Copy of *"Search and Rescue"*

L
Loading Check List

Weights

1. Basic empty weight of airplane ———

2. Weight of usable fuel (multiply six pounds per gallon of gasoline) ———

3. Weight of oil (multiply 7.5 pounds per *gallon*—not quart) ———

4. List each passenger with the weight of each
   1. Name _____ ———
   2. Name _____ ———
   3. Name _____ ———
   4. Name _____ ———
   5. Name _____ ———

5. List each suitcase with the weight of each (remember that weights of each may change after a RON)
   1. Description _____ ———
   2. Description _____ ———
   3. Description _____ ———
   4. Description _____ ———

6. List each item to be packed with the weight beside each. (skis, cameras, etc.)
   1. Description _____ ———
   2. Description _____ ———

Total of *all* weights ———

Gross weight allowed for plane ———

TOTAL WEIGHT MUST NOT BE A LARGER NUMBER THAN GROSS WEIGHT. *SOMETHING* MUST BE LEFT AT HOME.

	Weight Allowed	Weight of Person or Items
1. Front left seat	———	———
2. Front right seat	———	———
3. Second left seat	———	———
4. Second right seat	———	———
5. Third left seat	———	———
6. Third right seat	———	———
7. Front baggage compartment	———	———
8. Rear baggage compartment	———	———
Total	———	———

With the information furnished on this page, the pilot will be able to check very quickly the distribution of the load. You will soon become aware of proper balance with a little practice. Be sure that you weigh all items as it is amazing the weight of camera cases and women's purses.

M
Tools The Pilot Uses

Note: The majority of fixed base operators offer maps, computers, plotters, and other necessary equipment for the flying companion and the pilot. Following is a partial list of facilities that offer such services in the event no fixed base operator is nearby.

Aeronautique, 81 John Glenn Drive, Concord, Calif. 94520

Aero Publishers, Inc., 329 West Aviation Rd., Fallbrook, Calif. 92028

Aircraft Components Inc., North Shore Drive, Benton Harbor, Mich. 49022

Arnold Senterfitt, Rancho La Tierra, Lakeside, Calif. 92040 (Mexico and Baja California materials)

Aviation Owners and Pilots Association (AOPA), Box 5800, Washington, D.C. 20014

Department of Transportation, Federal Aviation Administration, Distribution Unit, TAD 484.3, Washington, D.C.
    Multiple circulars on requirements for owning and operating an aircraft (AC20-5B)
    Carbon monoxide (AC-20-32A)
    Prevention of landing gear failure (AC 20-34A)
    Propeller blade failure (AC 20-37A)
    Flight manuals, placards, listings, and instrument markings (AC 60-6)
    Fuel contamination (AC 20-43A)
    Know your aircraft (AC 60-1)
    Pilots spatial disorientation (AC 60-4)
    Severe weather avoidance (AC 90-12)
    Altitude-temperature effect on aircraft performance (AC 90-14A)
    Accidents in tricycle gear aircraft (AC 90-34)
    Use of oxygen (AC 91-8A)
    Drug hazards (AC 91.11-1)
    Cold weather operation (AC 91-13A)
    All of the above may be obtained without charge

Federal Aviation Administration Aeronautical Center, Operations Branch, AC-740, P.O. Box 25082, Oklahoma City, Oklahoma 73125
    Exam-O-Grams (these may be obtained without charge)

1976 Flying Annual and Pilot's Buying Guide, Flying, P.O. Box 2900, Clinton, Iowa 52732

Jeppesen & Co., 8025 East 40th Ave., Denver, Colo. 80207

National Ocean Survey, Distribution Division (C-44), Riverdale, Md. 20840
    Sectional charts, En Route charts, Area charts, Approach plates (by subscription)

National Pilot's Association, 806 15th St., N.W., Washington, D.C. 20005

PDQ Computer Co., Dept. A, Box 453, Asbury Park, N.J.

Pilot Shopper, Edgewater Institute, Box 25351, Los Angeles, Calif. 90025

Sky Prints, Dept. 1, 5743 W. Park, St. Louis, Mo. 63110

Superintendent of Documents, U.S. Government Printing Office, Washington, D.C. 20402
    Personal Aircraft Inspection Handbook (AC 20-9), $1.00
    Private Pilot's Handbook of Aeronautical Knowledge (AC 61-23) $2.75
    Instrument Flying Handbook (AC 61-27A) $2.50
    Aviation Weather (AC 00-6) $4.00